Monumental Inscriptions on the Web

A Directory

Stuart A. Raymond

FEDERATION OF FAMILY HISTORY SOCIETIES (PUBLICATIONS) LIMITED

Published by
The Federation of Family History Societies (Publications) Ltd
Units 15-16, Chesham Industrial Centre
Oram Street, Bury
Lancashire BL9 6EN

in association with
S.A. & M.J. Raymond
P.O. Box 35
Exeter, EX1 3YZ
Email: samjraymond@btopenworld.com

ISBNs:
Federation of Family History Societies 1-86006-169-9
S.A. & M.J. Raymond: 1-899668-30-6

First published 2002

Printed and bound by Alpha Print, Crawley Mill, Witney, Oxfordshire OX8 5TJ

Contents

Introduction

Every genealogist appreciates the value of monumental inscriptions. They frequently provide more information on relationships than official parish and civil registers, and their epitaphs may have something to say about the individual(s) buried. A rapidly increasing number of web-sites are devoted to monumental inscriptions, and it is the purpose of this directory to identify them, and to indicate where they may be found. Pages rather than sites are listed, since one site may contain many pages devoted to different places.

Arrangement of this directory is by county. Within each county, pages of general interest are listed first, under sub-headings such as 'web-page collections', 'indexes', 'publications', 'look-ups', *etc.* These are followed by an alphabetical listing of local pages.

The titles of each web-page are given as they appear on the page. If no title is given on the page, I have indicated this by enclosing my own wording in square brackets. Where the page is taken from a published book, this has been indicated.

Some of the pages listed here provide a complete record of inscriptions in the particular place covered. Many others, however, only provide extracts - and do not always indicate that this is the case. Some are in the course of construction, and should be re-checked every few months for new additions. It should also be realised that information on the web is liable to human error, and that electronic wizardry does not guarantee accuracy. If at all possible, you should always go back to the original inscription and check it, unless of course, you have found a photograph on the web.

I have tried to make this directory as comprehensive as possible. However, it is likely that I have missed some sites, and it is also the case that new sites appear every day. Furthermore, URL's change frequently, and no doubt a small proportion of those listed here will be out of date within a few months of publication. If you come across new pages that ought to be listed here, URL's that have changed, or errors in this directory, please let me know. It is hoped to produce new editions at frequent intervals, in order to help you keep track of the information currently available on the web.

This book has been typed by Cynthia Hanson, and seen through the press by Bob Boyd. My thanks go to them, and to the officers of the Federation of Family History Societies, whose support is vital to my work. My wife Marjorie is also to be thanked for insisting that I turn off the computer occasionally!

Stuart A. Raymond

General

- Find a Grave
  www.findagrave.com
  International; over 2,000 pages for individual English graves, plus many more overseas

- Monumental Inscriptions
  www.jaydax.co.uk/genlinks/
  Click on title

- Some notes on Medieval English Genealogy: Funeral Monuments
  www.medievalgenealogy.org.uk/guide.fun.html
  Introductory notes

- Recording Monumental Inscriptions
  www.neep.demon.co.uk/mis/recording.htm

- Transcribing Monumental Inscriptions
  www.muir.clara.net/record/

- Church Monuments Society
  freespace.virgin.net/john.bromilow/CMS/index.html

- The Ecclesiological Society
  www.ecclsoc.org

Gateways

- England Tombstone Project
  www.rootsweb.com/~engcemet/
  Links to sites for larger cemeteries

- Genealogy Resources on the Internet: Cemeteries/Monuments/Obituaries mailing lists
  www.rootsweb.com/~jfuller/gen__mail__cemetery.html
  List of lists, mainly overseas, but some of English interest

- Tombstones & Monumental Inscriptions
  gye.future.easyspace.com
  Gateway

Web Page Collections

- Gravestone Photographic Resource
  www.gravestonephotos.com/
  Collection of webpages, separately listed below

- Rosemary Lockie's Memorial Inscription Collection
  www.wishful-thinking.org.uk/Mls/
  Pages for Derbyshire, Gloucestershire, Herefordshire and Somerset

- Interment.net: Cemeteries of England
  www.interment.net/uk/eng.index.htm

- Old Roots Genealogy: Monumental Inscriptions Online
  www.oldroots.co.uk/inscriptions/

- Monumental Inscriptions
  www.towball.freewire.co.uk/monu.htm
  Collection of contributed inscriptions from various counties

Brasses

- Monumental Brasses on the Internet
  www.medievalgenealogy.org.uk/sources/brasses.shtml
  Links to many sites, mainly for individual brasses

- Monumental Brass Society
  www.mbs-brasses.co.uk
  Includes a detailed bibliography of monumental brasses, with pages for each county

- The Department of Antiquities: Monumental Brasses
  www.ashmol.ox.ac.uk/ash/departments/antiquities/brass/
  Of the Ashmolean Museum, Oxford

- A Gallery of Brass Rubbings
  ashweb.ashmol.ox.ac.uk/ash/departments/antiquities/brass/
  brass01a.htm

- The County series: a series of fully illustrated guides to the monumental brasses of the British Isles
  home.clara.net/williamlack/index.htm
  Details of a series of books

Bedfordshire

Brasses
- Bedfordshire
  www.mbs-brasses.co.uk/bedfordshire.htm
  Bibliography of monumental brasses

- Monumental Brass Rubbings for England: Bedfordshire
  www.ashmol.co.uk/ash/departments/antiquities/brass
  Click on 'Catalogue' and county. In the Ashmolean Museum, Oxford

Publications
- Bedfordshire Family History Society: Microfiche
  www.bfhs.org.uk/
  Click on 'Publication List' and 'B.F.H.S. Microfiche'. Includes many monumental inscriptions

Toddington
- Toddington Family History Resource Page: Memorial Inscriptions at Toddington Churchyard recorded circa 1900.
  www.toddington.net/memorial.htm

Turvey
- Monuments in Turvey Church
  www.turvey.homestead.com/monu1.html

Berkshire

Indexes
- Berkshire
  www.towball.freewire.co.uk/berk.htm
  Index of monumental inscriptions, mainly Compton, Datchet, Warfield, *etc.*

Publications
- Berkshire Monumental Inscriptions Project
  www.berkshirefhs.org.uk/projects/
  BerkshireMonumentalInscriptionsProject.htm
  Includes details of fiche available

Brasses
- Monumental Brass Rubbings for England: Berkshire
  www.ashmol.co.uk/ash/departments/antiquities/brass/
  Click on 'Catalogue' and county. In the Ashmolean Museum, Oxford

- Berkshire
  www.mbs-brasses.co.uk/berkshire.htm
  Bibliography of monumental brasses

Clewer
- A History of Clewer 6: the Churchyard
  home.clara.net/iainkerr/clewer/booklets/churchyard.htm

Compton
- Inscriptions from St. Mary's & St. Nicholas, Compton, Berkshire
  www.towball.co.uk/inscri18.htm
  Selected inscriptions

Datchet
- Inscriptions from St. Mary the Virgin, Datchet, Berkshire
  www.towball.co.uk/inscri20.htm
  Selected inscriptions

South Moreton
- Inscriptions from St. John the Baptist Church, South Moreton
  www.towball.freewire.co.uk/inscr__9.html
  Selected inscriptions

Wallingford
- Inscriptions from St. Mary Le More, Wallingford, Oxfordshire
  www.towball.freewire.co.uk/inscri__14.htm
  Selected inscriptions

Warfield
- Inscriptions from St. Michael the Archangel, Warfield, Berkshire
  www.towball.freewire.co.uk/inscri16.htm
  Selected inscriptions

Buckinghamshire

Indexes
- Monumental Inscriptions Database
  www.bucksfhs.org.uk/dmis0001.htm
  Offline searches from Buckinghamshire Family History Society

Brasses
- Monumental Brass Rubbings for England: Buckinghamshire
  www.ashmol.co.uk/ash/departments/antiquities/brass/
  Click on 'catalogue' and county. In the Ashmolean Museum, Oxford

- Buckinghamshire
  www.mbs-brasses.co.uk/Buckinghamshire.htm
  Bibliography of monumental brasses

Publications
- The Monumental Brasses of Buckinghamshire
  home.clara.net/williamlack/pages/bucks.htm
  Details of a book

Aylesbury
- Monumental Inscriptions: the Parish Church of St. Mary, Aylesbury
  met.open.ac.uk/genuki/big/eng/BKM/Aylesbury/mis/stmary.html

- Monumental Inscriptions, Castle Street Chapel, Aylesbury
  met.open.ac.uk/genuki/big/eng/BKM/Aylesbury/mis/CastleStreet.html

- Monumental Inscriptions Walton Street Baptist Chapel, Aylesbury
  met.open.ac.uk/genuki/big/eng/BKM/Aylesbury/mis/WaltonStreet.html

- Monumental Inscriptions: Hale Leys Chapel, Aylesbury
  met.open.ac.uk/big/eng/BKM/Aylesbury/mis/Haleleys.html

Bierton
- Monumental Inscriptions in the Parish Church of St. James the Great, Bierton
  met.open.ac.uk/genuki/big/eng/BKM/Bierton/Mls.html

Bledlow
- Monumental Inscriptions in the Parish Church of Bledlow
  met.open.ac.uk/genuki/big/eng/BKM/Mls.html
  Recorded in 1847

Bletchley
- Monumental Inscriptions in the Parish Church of St. Mary, Bletchley
  met.open.ac.uk/genuki/big/eng/BKM/Bletchley/Mls1.html

Calverton
- The Monumental Inscriptions Survey for the Church of All Saints, Calverton, Buckinghamshire, UK
  www.xor.org.uk/calverton/crj97/crj__20.htm
  Index

Horton
- Churchyard Monumental Inscriptions from St. Michael, Horton
  met.open.ac.uk/genuki/big/eng/BKM/horton/Mls.html
  Recorded in 1862

Wraysbury
- Churchyard Monumental Inscriptions from St. Andrew, Wraysbury
  met.open.ac.uk/genuki/big/eng/BKM/Wraysbury/Mls.html

Cambridgeshire

Indexes
- Monumental Inscriptions: Cambridgeshire
  www.towball.freewire.co.uk/cambridge.htm
  Index, mainly from Dullingham and Linton, but more may be added

Brasses
- Monumental Brass Rubbings for England: Cambridgeshire
  www.ashmol.co.uk/ash/departments/antiquities/brass/
  Clcik on 'Catalogue' and county. In the Ashmolean Museum, Oxford

- Cambridgeshire
  www.mbs-brasses.co.uk/Cambridgeshire.htm
  Bibliography of monumental brasses

Publications
- Cambridgeshire Family History Society: Monumental Inscriptions Microfiche
  www.personal.u-net.com/~gaer/cam/cfhs/mi__fiche.html

Dullingham
- Inscriptions from St. Mary's, Dullingham, Cambridge
  www.towball.freewire.co.uk/inscri21.html
  Selected inscriptions

Linton
- Inscriptions from St. Mary the Virgin, Linton, Cambridge
  www.towball.freewire.co.uk/inscri22.htm
  Selected inscriptions

Wimpole
- The Wimpole Registers: the Parish Churchyard Register: Index to named graves, monumental inscriptions, known unmarked graves, and the church vault.
  www.wimpole.ac.uk/churchyard.htm

Cheshire

Indexes
- North Cheshire Family History Society: Memorial Inscriptions Index
  www.genuki.org.uk/big/eng/CHS/NorthChesFHS/meminscr.htm
  Details of a search service

- Cemetery Surname Indexes, Cheshire, England
  freespace.virgin.net/tt.indexes/freebies/chesmi
  List of surnames found on fiche transcriptions of monumental inscriptions for Barnton, Barnston, Congleton, Little Budworth, Marston and Nantwich

Brasses
- Monumental Brass Rubbings for England: Cheshire
  www.ashmol.co.uk/ash/departments/antiquities/brass/
  Click on 'Catalogue' and county. In the Ashmolean Museum, Oxford

- Cheshire
  www.mbs-brasses.co.uk/cheshire.htm
  Bibliography of monumental brasses

Collections of Web-Pages
- Carl's Cam Graveyards & Cemeteries
  www.carlscam.com/graves.htm
  Collection of pages separately listed below

Publications
- Cheshire Monumental Inscriptions on Microfiche
  www.genuki.org.uk/big/eng/CHS/NorthChesFHS/microfiche__list.htm

- Family History Society of Cheshire: Microfiche Publications
  www.fhsc.org.uk/fich.htm
  Mainly monumental inscriptions and parish registers

- South Cheshire Family History Society Publications
  www.scfhs.org.uk/pubs.html
  Includes parish registers and monumental inscriptions

Buglawton
- Carl's Cam: Graveyards & Cemeteries: St. John the Evangelist, Buglawton
  www.carlscam.com/graves.htm
  Click on place. Photograph with a few transcriptions

Chadkirk
- Carls Cam Graveyards & Cemeteres: Chadkirk, near Romiley
  www.carlscam.com/graves.htm
  Click on 'Chadkirk'

Chester
- Overleigh Cemetery, Chester, England
  www.pharmcat.demon.co.uk/cemetery/over/index.htm
  Introduction only

Dukinfield
- Carl's Cam Graveyards & Cemeteries: Dukinfield Cemetery, Dukinfield, Cheshire
  www.carlscam.com/graves.htm
  Click on 'Cemetery' (under Dukinfield)

Godley
- Carl's Cam Graveyards & Cemeteries: St. John the Baptist, Godley, Hyde, Cheshire
  www.carlscam.com/graves.htm
  Click on 'St. John the Baptist'

Hatherlow
- Carl's Cam Graveyards & Cemeteries: Hatherlow Church
  www.carlscam.com/graves.html
  Click on 'Independent Church'

Macclesfield
- Carl's Cam Graveyards & Cemeteries: St. Michael & All Angels, Macclesfield, Cheshire
  www.carlscam.com/graves.html
  Click on 'St. Michael's Church'

- Macclesfield Cemetery
  users.net1plus.com/steff/gravesite.htm
  Photographs only

Marple
- Marple War Memorial
  www.marple-uk.com/memorial.htm

Over Cotton
- Memorial: Over Cotton Mill Disaster, 1874
  www.carlscam.com/memo.htm
  Click on place

Stockport
- Carl's Cam Graveyards & Cemeteries: St. Mary's, Stockport, Cheshire
  www.carlscam.com/graves.htm
  Click on ' St. Mary's'

- Carl's Cam Graveyards & Cemeteries: Stockport Municipal Cemetery, Cheshire
  www.carlscam.com/graves.htm
  Click on 'Municipal Cemetery'

Taxal
- Carl's Cam Graveyards & Cemeteries: St. James, Taxal
  www.carlscam.com/graves.htm
  Click on 'St. James Church'

Tintwistle
- Carl's Cam Graveyards & Cemeteries: Old Chapel Yard, Tintwistle, Cheshire
  www.carlscam.com/graves.htm
  Click on 'Old Chapel Yard'

Wirral
- Flaybrick Hill Cemetery, Wirral, England
  www.pharmcat.demon.co.uk/cemetery/flay/index.htm
  Introduction only

Woodhead
- Carl's Cam Graveyards & Cemeteries: St. James Chapel, Woodhead, Cheshire
  www.carlscam.com/graves.htm
  Click on 'St. James Chapel'

Cornwall

Indexes
- Cornish Cemeteries
  chrisuphill.tripod.com/
  Combined index to inscriptions at Barnoon Cemetery, Callington Churchyard, Camborne Centenary Wesleyan Cemetery, Camborne Parish Church, Crowan Cemetery, St. Euny, Landrake Churchyard, Longstone Cemetery, Penponds Cemetery, Phillack Cemetery, Quethiock Parish Church and Towednack Churchyard

- Cornish Cemeteries
  freepages.genealogy.rootsweb.com/~chrisu/cemeteries.htm

Brasses
- Monumental Brass Rubbings for England: Cornwall
  www.ashmol.co.uk/ash/departments/antiquities/brass/
  Click on 'Catalogue' and county. In the Ashmolean Museum, Oxford

- Cornwall
  www.mbs-brasses.co.uk/Cornwall.htm
  Bibliography of monumental brasses

Web Page Collections
- Burials in Cornwall
  freepages.genealogy.rootsweb.com/~framland/con/cornindex.htm
  Collection of monumental inscription web-pages, each listed separately below

Caerhays
- Caerhays Church Gravestone Inscriptions
  www.gorran-haven.com/caerinsc__1.htm

Camborne
- Camborne Memorial Inscriptions
  ourworld.compuserve.com/homepages/jon__rees/camborne__mi.htm

Crowan
- Crowan Cemetery
  freepages.genealogy.rootsweb.com/~chrisu/cwn1.htm
  Index to inscriptions. Continued on 4 further pages

Illogan

- Parish Church Burial Ground Records (from 1895)
www.saint-illogan.org.uk/records.htm#t1

- Illogan memorial inscriptions
ourworld.compuserve.com/homepages/jon__rees/illogan__mi.htm
Includes 2483 surnames

Lamorran

- Lamorran monument inscriptions
www.cornish-ancestors.co.uk/Lamorran/Misc%20Information/
monument__inscriptions.htm

Lostwithiel

See St. Stephen in Brannel

Mevagissey

- Mevagissey Old Cemetery Gravestone Inscriptions
www.gorran-haven.com/mevinscr.htm

- Trewinney Cemetery, Mevagissey
www.gorran-haven.com/trewhinney.htm
20th c.

Morwenstow

- The Parish Church of St. John the Baptist and St. Morwenna
www.morwenstow.freeserve.co.uk/Morwenstow/MPC/MPChome.htm
In progress. Morwenstow monumental inscriptions

- Woodford Bible Christian Chapel
www.morwenstow.freeserve.co.uk/WBC/WBC__Home.html
Monumental inscriptions at a Morwenstow chapel

- MIs: Woodford (Bible Christian) Chapel
www.genuki.org.uk/big/eng/Cornwall/Morwenstow/WoodfordBC__MI.html

- Woodford Wesleyan Chapel
www.morwenstow.freeserve.co.uk/Morwenstow/WWC/WWC__home.htm
Monumental inscriptions at a Morwenstow chapel

- MIs: Woodford (Weslyan) Chapel
www.genuki.org.uk/big/eng/Cornwall/Morwenstow/WoodfordWes__MI.html

- **Shop Methodist Chapel**
www.morwenstow.freeserve.co.uk/Morwenstow/SMC/SMChome.html
Monumental inscriptions at a Morwenstow chapel

- Monumental Inscriptions: Shopford Methodist Church, Morwenstow
www.genuki.org.uk/big/eng/Cornwall/Morwenstow/Shop__MI.html

Phillack

- Phillack
freepages.genealogy.rootsweb.com/chrisu/phil1.htm
Index to inscriptions. Continued on 5 further pages

- Monumental Inscriptions
freepages.genealogy.rootsweb.com/~jwheeler/
monumentalinscriptions.htm
For Phillack

Philleigh

- Philleigh Monument Inscriptions
www.cornish-ancestors.co.uk/Philleigh/Misc%20Information/
monument__inscriptions.htm

Redruth

- St. Day Rd, Redruth Memorial Inscriptions
ourworld.compuserve.com/homepages/jon__rees/stdayx.htm

- St. Euny, Redruth
freepages.rootsweb.com/~chrisu/eun1.htm
Index to inscriptions. Continued on 6 further pages

- St. Euny (Redruth) Memorial Inscriptions
oneworld.compuserve.com/homepages/jon__rees/steuny.htm

St. Breock

- St. Breock Monumental Inscriptions
slapster2.tripod.com/mi__link.htm

St. Erth

- Monument Inscriptions for St. Erth
freepages.genealogy.rootsweb.com/~juneen/sterth.html

St. Eval

- Around St. Eval
freepages.genealogy.rootsweb.com/~cornwall/parish/evall.htm
Includes monumental inscriptions

St. Ewe
- St. Ewe Gravestone Inscriptions
  www.gorran-haven.com/steweinsc.htm

St. Stephen in Brannel
- Monumental Inscriptions
  www.caerkief.demon.co.uk/monum.htm
  From St. Stephen in Brannel, Treverbyn, and Lostwithiel. Incomplete.

Towednack
- Monument Inscriptions for Towednack
  freepages.genealogy.rootsweb.com/~juneen/tow.html

Treleigh
- Treleigh Memorial Inscriptions
  ourworld.compuserve.com/homepages/jon__rees/treleighx.htm

Treverbyn
See St. Stephen in Brannel

Tuckingmill
- Monument Inscriptions for Tuckingmill
  freepages.genealogy.rootsweb.com/~juneen/tuck.html

Cumberland

Institutional Collections
- Cumbrian Burials: Memorial Inscription Records available at Cumbrian Record Offices
  edenlinks.rootsweb.com/1gp/RECORDS/MS.HTM

Web Page Collections
- Monuments and Memorials in Cumbria
  www.orrison.com/genealogy/monuments/index.html
  Little here as yet, but pages of memorial photos and transcriptions planned.

Brasses
- Monumental Brass Rubbings for England: Cumberland
  www.ashmol.co.uk/ash/departments/antiquities/brass/
  Click on 'Catalogue' and county. In the Ashmolean Museum, Oxford

- Cumberland
  www.mbs-brasses.co.uk/Cumberland.htm
  Bibliography of monumental brasses

Aikton
- Monumental Inscriptions, Aikton, Cumberland
  freepages.genealogy.rootsweb.com/~brianmiller/BMD/DEA/
  Aikton__MI.htm

Ennerdale
- Ennerdale Churchyard, Cumbria County, England
  www.interment.net/data/eng/cumbria/ennerdale/ennerdale.htm

Penrith
- Penrith Memorial Indexing Project
  www.zeonlair.demon.co.uk/famtree/penrith.htm

Derbyshire

Web Page Collections
- The Derbyshire Ancestral Research Group Memorial Inscriptions
  www.genuki.org.uk/big/eng/DBY/DARG/MIs.html
  List of transcriptions held including a few online indexes

- Monumental Inscriptions: Derbyshire
  www.towball.freewire.co.uk/Derbyshire.htm
  Index to selected inscriptions; only Heath is included at present, but more may be added

- Wishful Thinking's GENUKI: Derbyshire Pages: Memorial Inscriptions Collection
  www.wishful-thinking.org.uk/genuki/DBY/MIs.html
  Pages individually listed below

Brasses
- Monumental Brass Rubbings for England: Derbyshire
  www.ashmol.co.uk/ash/departments/antiquities/brass/
  Click on 'Catalogue' and county. In the Ashmolean Museum, Oxford

- Derbyshire
  www.mbs-brasses.co.uk/Derbyshire.htm
  Bibliography of monumental brasses

- The Monumental Brasses of Derbyshire
  home.clara.net/williamlack/pages.derbys.htm
  Details of a book

Publications
- Derbyshire Family History Society Publications List ... Memorial Inscription Publications
  www.dfhs.org.uk/publics/dfhsmis.htm

Alkmonton
- Some Memorial Inscriptions: Alkmonton, Derbyshire: St. John's Churchyard
  www.wishful-thinking.org.uk/Genuki/DBY/Alkmonton/MIs.html

Ashbourne
- Some Memorial Inscriptions: Ashbourne, Derbyshire: St. Oswald's Churchyard and Cemetery
  www.wishful-thinking.org.uk/Genuki/DBY/Ashbourne/MIs.html

Barlow
- Some Memorial Inscriptions: Barlow, Derbyshire. St. Lawrence's Churchyard
  www.wishful-thinking.org.uk/genuki/DBY/Barlow/MIs.html

Baslow
- Some Memorial Inscriptions, Baslow, Derbyshire: St. Anne's Churchyard
  www.wishful-thinking.org.uk/genuki/DBY/Baslow/MIs.html

Boylestone
- Some Memorial Inscriptions: Boylestone, Derbyshire: St. John the Baptists Churchyard
  www.wishful-thinking.org.uk/genuki/DBY/Boylestone/MIs.html

Brailsford
- Some Memorial Inscriptions: Brailsford, Derbyshire: All Saints Churchyard
  www.wishful-thinking.org.uk/genuki/DBY/Brailsford/MIs.html

Brassington
- Monumental Inscriptions in Brassington Churchyard
  www.brassington.org./monument.htm

Chellaston
- Chellaston Monumental Inscriptions
  freepages.genealogy.rootsweb.com/~brett/chellaston/chellaston__mi.htm

Chelmorton
- Surnames from the Memorial Inscriptions of St. John the Baptist Chelmorton
  www.genuki.org.uk/big/eng/DBY/DARG/ChelmortonMIs.html

Chesterfield
- Surnames from the Memorial Inscriptions of the Church of Holy Trinity, Chesterfield
  www.genuki.org.uk/big/eng/DBY/DARG/ChesterfieldMIs.html

Chinley

- Surnames from the Gravestones at White Knowle (Chinley)
  www.genuki.org.uk/big/eng/DBY/DARG/WhiteknowleMIs.html

Clowne

- Surnames from the Monumental Inscriptions of St. John the Baptist, Clowne
  www.genuki.org.uk/big/eng/DBE/DARG/ClowneMIs.html

Crich

- Memorials
  freepages.genealogy.rootsweb.com/~dlhdby/memorial.htm
  At Crich

Cubley

- Some Memorial Inscriptions: Cubley, Derbyshire: St. Andrew's Churchyard
  www.wishful-thinking.org.uk/Genuki/DBY/Cubley/MIs.html

Curbar

- Surnames from the Monumental Inscriptions of the church of All Saints, Curbar
  www.genuki.org.uk/big/eng/DBY/DARG/CurbarMIs.html

- Some Memorial Inscriptions: Curbar, Derbyshire: All Saints churchyard
  www.wishful-thinking.org.uk/genuki/DBY/Curbar/MIs.html

Denby

- Surnames from the Memorial Inscriptions of St. Mary the Virgin, Denby
  www.genuki.org.uk/big/eng/DBY/DARG/DenbyMIs.html

Derby

- Derby: our oldest cemetery
  www.derbycity.com/derby/tombs.html
  Brief notes on Uttoxeter Road Cemetery, Derby with a few photographs

Donisthorpe

- St. John's, Donisthorpe Monumental Inscriptions
  freepages.genealogy.rootsweb.com/~brett/donisthorpe/
  donisthorpe__mi.html

Dronfield

- Some Memorial Inscriptions: Dronfield, Derbyshire: St. John the Baptist Churchyard
  www.wishful-thinking.org.uk/genuki/DBY/Dronfield/MIs.html

Duffield

- Monuments
  www.derwent99.freeserve.co.uk/duffield10mon.htm
  Lecture notes on Duffield monuments

Edensor

- Some Memorial Inscriptions: Edensor, Derbyshire: St. Peter's Churchyard
  www.wishful-thinking.org.uk/Genuki/DBY/Edensor/MIs.html

Egginton

- Surnames from the Memorial Inscriptions of St. Wilfrid, Egginton
  www.genuki.org.uk/big/eng/DBY/DARG/EggintonMIs.html

Eyam

- The History and Antiquities of Eyam: the Churchyard
  www.genuki.org.uk/big/eng/DBY/Eyam/Wood/Churchyard.html
  Includes some inscriptions. For a page on the church, also including inscriptions, visit **/Church.html**

- Some Memorial Inscriptions: Eyam, Derbyshire. St. Lawrence Churchyard
  www.wishful-thinking.org.uk/genuki/DBY/Eyam/MIs.html

Grindleford

- Some Memorial Inscriptions: Grindleford, Derbyshire: St. Helen's Churchyard
  www.wishful-thinking.org.uk/genuki/DBY/Grindleford/MIs.html

Hartington
- Surname from the Memorial Inscriptions of St. Giles, Hartington
  www.genuki.org.uk/big/eng/DBY/DARG/HartingtonMIs.html

Hathersage
- Some Memorial Inscriptions: Hathersage, Derbyshire. St. Michael & All Angels Churchyard
  www.wishful-thinking.org.uk/Hathersage/MIs.html

Heath
- Inscriptions from Heath Church
  www.towball.freewire.co.uk/inscri__1.htm

Hope
- Monumental Inscriptions: St. Peter's Church, Hope, Derbyshire, UK
  www.coplowdale.fsnet.co.uk/Blank%20Page%206.htm
  Photographs of a few gravestones

Horsley
- Surnames from the Memorial Inscriptions of St. Clements, Horsley
  www.genuki.org.uk/big/eng/DBY/DARG/HorsleyMIs.html

Matlock
- Matlock and Matlock Bath, Derbyshire: Memorial Inscriptions Surnames Index
  www.andrewspages.dial.pipex.com/matlock/mi.htm

Monyash
- Some Memorial Inscriptions: Monyash, Derbyshire: St. Leonard's Churchyard
  www.wishful-thinking.org.uk/Genuki/DBY/Monyash/MIs.html

Norbury
- Some Memorial Inscriptions: Norbury, Derbyshire: St. Mary & St. Barlok's Churchyard
  www.wishful-thinking.org.uk/Genuki/DBY/Norbury/MIs.html

Old Brampton
- Some Memorial Inscriptions: Old Brampton, Derbyshire. St. Peter & St. Paul's Churchyard
  www.wishful-thinking.org.uk/genuki/DBY/OldBrampton/MIs.html

Overseal
- Overseal St. Matthew Memorial Inscriptions
  freepages.genealogy.rootsweb.com/~brett/seal/overseal__mi.html

Parwich
- Search the Parwich Graveyard
  www.parwichchurch.co.uk/searchpage.asp

- Surnames from the Memorial Inscriptions at St. Peter's, Parwich
  www.genuki.org.uk/big/eng/DBY/DARG/ParwichMIs.html

Peak Forest
- Surnames from the Memorial Inscriptions of St. Charles, King and Martyr, Peak Forest
  www.genuki.org.uk/big/eng/DBY/DARG/PeakForestMIs.html

Shirley
- Some Memorial Inscriptions: Shirley, Derbyshire: St. Michael's Churchyard
  www.wishful-thinking.org.uk/Genuki/DBY/Shirley/MIs.html

Somercotes
- Surnames from the Memorial Inscriptions of Birchwood Lane, Somercotes
  www.genuki.org.uk/big/eng/DBY/DARG/BirchwoodMIs.html

Spondon
- The Surnames from the Gravestones at St. Werburgh's and Chapel Street
  www.genuki.org.uk/big/eng/DBY/DARG/SpondonMIs.html
  At Spondon

Stanley
- Surnames from the Memorial Inscriptions of the Church of St. Andrew, Stanley
  www.genuki.org.uk/big/eng/DBY/DARG/StanleyMIs.html

- Memorial Inscriptions for Stanley and Stanley Common
  freepages.genealogy.rootsweb.com/~alanbloor/MIhome.htm

Stoney Middleton
- Some Memorial Inscriptions, Stoney Middleton, Derbyshire: St. Martin's Churchyard and Cemetery
  www.wishful-thinking.org.uk/genuki/DBY/StoneyMiddleton/Mls.html

Tibshelf
- Surnames from the Memorial Inscriptions of St. John the Baptist, Tibshelf
  www.genuki.org.uk/big/eng/DBY/DARG/TibshelfMls.html

Wardlow
- Some Memorial Inscriptions: Wardlow, Derbyshire, Church of the Good Shepherd
  www.wishful-thinking.org.uk/genuki/DBY/Wardlow/Mls.html

Whitwell
- Surnames from the Gravestones at Steetley Chapel (Whitwell)
  www.genuki.org.uk/big/eng/DBY/DARG/SteetleyMls.html

Wirksworth
- Surnames from the Memorial Inscriptions of Wirksworth Cemetery and Church
  www.genuki.org.uk/big/eng/DBY/DARG/WirksworthMls.html

Yeaveley
- Some Memorial Inscriptions: Yeaveley, Derbyshire: Holy Trinity Churchyard
  www.wishful-thinking.org.uk/Genuki/DBY/Yeaveley/Mls.html

Youlgreave
- Surnames from the Memorial Inscriptions of All Saints, Youlgreave
  www.genuki.org.uk/big/eng/DBY/DARG/YoulgreaveMls.html

Devon

General
- Lost Devon Monumental Inscriptions
  www.dartmoorpress.clara.net/indexlost.html

Brasses
- Monumental Brass Rubbings for England: Devon
  www.ashmol.co.uk/ash/departments/antiquities/brass/
  Click on 'Catalogue' and county. In the Ashmolean Museum, Oxford

- Devonshire
  www.mbs-brasses.co.uk/Devonshire.htm
  Bibliography of monumental brasses

Branscombe
See Stoke Damerel

Dartmoor
- Lost Devon (Dartmoor) monumental inscriptions
  www.dartmoorpress.clara.net/indexlost.html
  From many parishes

Dittisham
- Ancestral graves in Dittisham, Devon
  www.familynet.co.uk/services/case2.htm
  Brief transcripts of a few stones only

Doddiscombsleigh
- Doddiscombesleigh Gravestone Inscriptions
  homepages.ntlworld/sjfroud/
  Doddiscombesleigh%20gravestone%20inscriptions.html
  Brief extracts only

Dunsford
- Dunsford Gravestone Inscriptions
  homepage.ntlworld.com/sjfroud/
  Dunsford%20gravestone%20inscriptions.html
  Brief extracts only

Exeter
- The Jews Cemetery at Exeter
www.eclipse.co.uk/exeshul/exeshul/history/grounds.html
Includes photographs of every single tombstone

High Bickington
- Graves in St. Mary's Churchyard, High Bickington
www.high-bickington.org.uk/graves.htm

Kenton
- Kenton Gravestone Inscriptions
homepage.ntlworld.com/sjfroud/kenton.html

Landkey
- Trinity Church, Landkey Gravestones
www.cs.ncl.ac.uk/genuki/DEV/Landkey/LandkeyMIs.html

Marldon
- St. John the Baptist Church in Marldon, Devon
www.geocities.com/Athens/Acropolis/3033/marldon.html
List of surnames on gravestones

Northam
- Northam Monumental Inscriptions
www.cs.ncl.ac.uk/genuki/DEV/Northam/
MonumentalInscriptions/index.html

Petrockstowe
- Petrockstowe One Place Genealogy: Petrockstowe Churchyard
Monumental Inscriptions
www.petrockstowe.co.uk/monumental.html
Forthcoming

Plymouth
- Tombstone Inscriptions in the Old Jewish Cemetery on Plymouth Hoe
www.eclipse.co.uk/exeshul/susser/plymouthtombstones.htm

Stoke Damerel
- Inscriptions from Gravestones in Branscombe
www.cs.ncl.ac.uk/genuki/DEV/StokeDamerel/StokeDamerel-BranIMIs.html
Originally from Stoke Damerel's 'Milehouse' cemetery

Sutcombe
- Sutcombe Village Records
www.sutcomberecords.co.uk
Click on 'contents', and on 'Monumental Inscriptions'

Dorset

Cemeteries
- Dorset Cemeteries and Crematoria
  ukburials-cremations.co.uk/dorset__cem__crem.htm
  List for Bournemouth, Christchurch and Poole

Web Page Collection
- Dorset Monumental Inscriptions on Line
  www.btinternet.com/~wonr/oldroots/mi__dor.htm
  Very small on-line collection, but more may be added

Indexes
- Dorset Monumental Inscriptions
  www.sdfhs.org/Dormis.htm
  Details of an index to transcriptions held by Somerset & Dorset Family
  History Society

- Services [of Dorset Family History Society]
  www.dorsetfhs.freeserve.co.uk/Services.htm
  Includes details of the society's monumental inscriptions index

Brasses
- Monumental Brass Rubbings for England: Dorset
  www.ashmol.ac.uk/ash/departments/antiquities/brass/counties/
  Dorset.html

  In the Ashmolean Museum, Oxford

- Dorset
  www.mbs-brasses.co.uk/Dorset.htm
  Bibliography of monumental brasses

Tolpuddle
- St. John the Evangelist, Parish Church, Tolpuddle: Monumental
  Inscriptions
  www.life.clara.net/tolpud/graves.htm

Durham

Cemeteries
- Cemeteries of Durham Region
  durhamcemeteries.com/Cemeteries/
  Addresses and phone nos.

Institutional Collections
- Durham County Record Office Handlist 10. Monumental Inscriptions,
  Cemetery and Crematorium Registers, and Will Indexes
  www.durham.gov.uk/durhamcc/usp.nsf/lookup/pdfhandlists/$file/
  handlist10.pdf

- Tyne & Wear Archives User Guide 1. Cemeteries & Crematoria
  www.thenortheast.com/archives/UserGuides/01__Cemeteries.html
  Lists registers, monumental inscriptions, *etc.,* for Gateshead, Newcastle,
  North Tyneside, South Tyneside, and Sunderland

- Durham Monumental Inscriptions
  www.ndfhs.org.uk/Library/index.html
  Click on title. In the library of the Northumberland & Durham Family
  History Society

- Gateshead Council, Local Studies Department: Miscellaneous Records
  www.swinhope.demon.co.uk/genuki/DUR/GatesheadLib/misc.html
  Includes lists of 'church records: microfilms and transcripts'; also
  'transcriptions of epitaphs and gravestones'.

- Monumental Inscriptions. Genealogy Guide no. 6: Newcastle upon Tyne
  Local Studies Library
  www.swinhope.demon.co.uk/genuki/NBL/NCLLib/NCLGG6.html
  Covers Durham and Northumberland

- Durham Mining Museum: Disaster Memorials
  www.dmm.org.uk/memorial/
  Collection of photographs of memorials to miners

Brasses
- Monumental Brass Rubbings for England: Durham
  www.ashmol.co.uk/ash/departments/antiquities/brass/
  Click on 'Catalogue' and county. In the Ashmolean Museum, Oxford

- Durham
  www.mbs-brasses.co.uk/Durham.htm
  Bibliography of monumental brasses

Aycliffe
- Aycliffe Saint Andrew Churchyard, Aycliffe, Durham, England
  www.interment.net/data/eng/durham/aycliff__andrew.htm

Billingham
- Billingham Saint Cuthbert Churchyard, Stockton on Tees, Cleveland, England
  www.interment.net/data/eng/cleveland/cuthbert/cuthbert.htm

Bishop Middleham
- Bishop Middleham Saint Michael Churchyard, Stockton on Tees, Cleveland, England
  www.interment.net/data/eng/cleveland/stmichael/stmike.htm

Castle Eden
- Castle Eden Saint James Churchyard, Castle Eden, Durham, England
  www.interment.net/data/eng/durham/castleden/stjames.htm

Cockfield
- Cockfield Saint Mary Churchyard, Cockfield, Durham, England
  www.interment.net/data/eng/durham/cockfield__stmary/stmary.htm

Elwick Hall
- Elwick Hall Saint Peter Churchyard, Hartlepool, Durham, England
  www.interment.net/data/eng/durham/stpeter/stpeter.htm

Greatham
- Greatham Saint John Churchyard, Durham, England
  www.interment.net/data/eng/durham/saintjohn/john.htm

- Old Cemetery Greatham, Durham, England
  www.interment.net/data/eng/durham/greatham/greatham.htm

Hart
- Hart Saint Mary Magdelaine Churchyard, Stockton on Tees, Cleveland, England
  www.interment.net/data/eng/cleveland/stmary-hart/stmary.htm

Hartlepool
- North Cemetery, Durham, England
  www.interment.net/data/eng/durham/north/north.htm
  At Hart Lane, Hartlepool

- Hartlepool Spion Kop (Old) Cemetery, Hartlepool, Durham, England
  www.interment.net/data/eng/durham/spion__kop/spionkop.htm

- Saint Hilda Churchyard, Hartlepool, Durham, England
  www.interment.net/data/eng/durham/sthilda/hilda.htm

- West View Cemetery, Hartlepool, Durham, England
  www.interment.net/data/eng/durham/westview/westview.htm

Norton
- Norton Saint Mary Churchyard, Stockton on Tees, Cleveland, England
  www.interment.net/data/eng/cleveland/stmary-virgin/stmary.htm

Sedgefield
- Sedgefield Saint Edmund Churchyard, Stockton on Tees, Cleveland, England
  www.interment.net/data/eng/cleveland/edmund/edmund.htm

Stockton on Tees
- Stockton On Tees, Saint Thomas Parish Churchyard, Stockton On Tees, Cleveland, England
  www.interment.net/data/eng/cleveland/st__thomas/thomas.htm

- Durham Road Cemetery, Stockton On Tees, Cleveland, England
  www.interment.net/data/eng/cleveland/durham__rd/durham.htm

Stranton
- Stranton All Saints Churchyard, Hartlepool, Durham, England
  www.interment.net/data/eng/durham/allsaints/saints.htm

- Stranton Grange Cemetery, Hartlepool, Durham, England
  www.interment.net/data/eng/durham/stranton__grange/stranton.htm

Tanfield
- Monumental Inscriptions, Tanfield, Durham
  freepages.genealogy.rootsweb.com/~brianmiller/BMD/DEA/
  Tanfield__MI.htm

Wolviston

- Wolviston Saint Peter Churchyard, Stockton On Tees, Cleveland, England
  www.interment.net/data/eng/cleveland/stpeter/peter.htm

Essex

Cemeteries

- East of London Family History Society: East London Cemeteries and Crematoria
  eolfhs.rootsweb.com/eolcem02.htm
  In Essex, London and Middlesex

Brasses

- Monumental Brass Rubbings for England: Essex
  www.ashmol.co.uk/ash/departments/antiquities/brass/
  Click on 'Catalogue' and county. In the Ashmolean Museum, Oxford

- Essex
  www.mbs-brasses.co.uk/Essex.htm
  Bibliography of monumental brasses

Publications

- Essex Society for Family History: Essex Monumental Inscriptions
  www.esfh.org.uk/
  Click on 'Postal Bookshop' and 'Monumental Inscriptions'.
  Mainly fiche for sale

- The East of London Family History Society: Monumental Inscriptions on Microfiche
  eolfhs.rootsweb.com/pubmii.htm
  Relating to Essex and London

Great Horkesley

- All Saints, Great Horkesley Monumental Inscriptions
  homepages.rootsweb.com/~mwi/gthorkmi.txt

Kelvedon Hatch

- Kelvedon Hatch, Essex: Local and Family History: Transcript made of all inscriptions inside old St. Nicholas Church, January 1955
  www.historyhouse.co.uk/stnicholas.html

Gloucestershire and Bristol

Institutional Collections
- Catalogue of Memorial and Burial Sites for Gloucestershire
  www.cix.co.uk/~rd/GENUKI/mem-bur.htm
  Transcripts held, or for sale, by Gloucestershire Family History Society

- Gloucestershire Monumental Inscriptions
  www.neep.demon.co.uk/mis/glos/
  List of transcriptions completed and available from Gloucestershire Family History Society

Web Page Collections
- Wishful Thinking's GENUKI: Gloucestershire Page: Memorial Inscription Collection
  www.wishful-thinking.org.uk/genuki/GLS/Mls.html

Brasses
- Monumental Brass Rubbings for England: Gloucestershire
  www.ashmol.co.uk/ash/departments/antiquities/brass/
  Click on 'Catalogue' and county. In the Ashmolean Museum, Oxford

- Gloucestershire
  www.mbs-brasses.co.uk/Gloucestershire.htm
  Bibliography of monumental brasses

Publications
- Memorial Inscriptions
  www.cix.co.uk/~rd/GENUKI/meminsc2.htm
  List of disks/fiche for sale by Gloucestershire Family History Society

Alderley
- Some Memorial Inscriptions: Alderley, Gloucestershire: St. Kenelm's Churchyard
  www.wishful-thinking.org.uk/GLS/Alderley/Mls.html

Alderton
- Some Memorial Inscriptions: Alderton, Gloucestershire: St. Giles Churchyard
  www.wishful-thinking.org.uk/genuki/GLS/Alderton/Mls.html

Almondsbury
- Some Memorial Inscriptions: Almondsbury, Gloucestershire: St. Mary's Churchyard and Cemetery
  www.wishful-thinking.org.uk/genuki/GLS/Mls.html

Alveston
- Some Memorial Inscriptions: Alveston, Gloucestershire: St. Helen's Churchyard
  www.wishful-thinking.org.uk/genuki/GLS/Alveston/Mls.html

Ampney Crucis
- Some Memorial Inscriptions: Ampney Crucis, Gloucestershire: The Holy Rood Churchyard
  www.wishful-thinking.org.uk/genuki/GLS/AmpneyCrucis/Mls.html

Ampney St. Mary
- Some Memorial Inscriptions: Ampney St. Mary, Gloucestershire: St. Mary's Churchyard
  www.wishful-thinking.org.uk/genuki/GLS/AmpneyStMary/Mls.html

Ampney St. Peter
- Some Memorial Inscriptions: Ampney St. Peter, Gloucestershire: St. Peter's Churchyard
  www.wishful-thinking.org.uk/genuki/GLS/AmpneyStPeter.html

Arnos Vale
- Friends of Arnos Vale Cemetery
  www.favc.freeserve.co.uk/
  Bristol cemetery; introduction only

Ashchurch
- Some Memorial Inscriptions: Ashchurch, Gloucestershire: St. Nicholas's Churchyard
  www.wishful-thinking.org.uk/genuki/GLS/Ashchurch/Mls.html

Ashton under Hill
- Ashton-under-Hill, Gloucestershire, UK: Church of Saint Barbara: Monumental Inscriptions
  www.ukonline.co.uk/flight/ashtonmi.html
  Transcription originally published 1919

Aust

- Some Memorial Inscriptions: Aust, Gloucestershire: St. John's Churchyard
  www.wishful-thinking.org.uk/genuki/GLS/Aust/Mls.html

Avening

- Church Monuments at Avening
  www.grahamthomas.com/Avening.html

- Some Memorial Inscriptions: Avening, Gloucestershire. The Holy Cross Churchyard
  www.wishful-thinking.org.uk/genuki/GLS/Avening/Mls.html

Berkeley

- Some Memorial Inscriptions: Berkeley, Gloucestershire: St. Mary's Churchyard and Cemetery
  www.wishful-thinking.org.uk/genuki/GLS/Berkeley/Mls.html

Bisley

- Some Memorial Inscriptions: Bisley, Gloucestershire: All Saints Churchyard
  www.wishful-thinking.org.uk/genuki/GLS/Bisley/Mls.html

Blockley

- Blockley Churchyard Inscriptions
  members.shaw.ca/panthers2/BlockInscript.html

Bristol

See also Arnos Vale

- Bristol Cemetery Database
  www.jewishgen.org/databases/bristol.htm
  Jewish cemetery

Brockworth

- Brockworth, Gloucestershire, UK: Monumental Inscriptions 1880
  web.ukonline.co.uk/flight/brockworthmi.html

Cam

See also Dursley

Cam

- Some Memorial Inscriptions: Cam, Gloucestershire. St. George's Churchyard
  www.wishful-thinking.org.uk/genuki/GLS/Cam/Mls.html

Charfield

- Some Memorials Inscriptions: Charfield, Gloucestershire. St. Andrew's Churchyard
  www.wishful-thinking.org.uk/genuki/GLS/Charfield/Mls.html

- Some Memorial Inscriptions: Charfield, Gloucestershire: St. James' Churchyard and Congregational Church
  www.wishful-thinking.org.uk/genuki/GLS/Charfield/Mls.html

Charlton Kings

- Charlton Kings, Gloucestershire, UK: Monumental Inscriptions 1876
  web.ukonline.co.uk/flight/charltonmi.html
  Extracted from *Gloucestershire notes & queries,* 1881

Cheltenham

- Christ Church, Cheltenham, Monumental Inscriptions
  web.ukonline.co.uk/flight/cheltchristmi.html
  From *Gloucestershire notes & queries*

Cherington

- Cherington Church and Monuments
  www.grahamthomas.com/cherington.html

- Some Memorial Inscriptions: Cherington, Gloucestershire: St. Nicholas' Churchyard
  www.wishful-thinking.org.uk/genuki/GLS/Cherington/Mls.html

Chipping Campden

- Chipping Campden Churchyard Inscriptions
  members.shaw.ca/panthers2/Chipinscript.html
  Originally published 1911

Chipping Sodbury

- Some Memorial Inscriptions: Chipping Sodbury, Gloucestershire. Cemetery
  www.wishful-thinking.org.uk/genuki/GLS/ChippingSodbury/Mls.html

Cinderford
- Some Memorial Inscriptions: Cinderford, Gloucestershire: St. John's Churchyard
  www.wishful-thinking.org.uk/genuki/GLS/Cinderford/MIs.html

Coaley
- Some Memorial Inscriptions: Coaley, Gloucestershire. St. Bartholomew's Churchyard
  www.wishful-thinking.org.uk/genuki/GLS/Coaley/MIs.html

Coleford
- Some Memorial Inscriptions: Coleford, Gloucestershire: Cemetery
  www.wishful-thinking.org.uk/genuki/GLS/Coleford/MIs.html

Cromhall
- Some Memorial Inscriptions: Cromhall, Gloucestershire. St. Andrew's Churchyard
  www.wishful-thinking.org.uk/genuki/GLS/Cromhall/MIs.html

Didmarton
- Some Memorial Inscriptions: Didmarton, Gloucestershire. St. Lawrence's Churchyard
  www.wishful-thinking.org.uk/genuki/GLS/Didmarton/MIs.html

Dursley
- Dursley, Gloucestershire & neighbourhood
  web.ukonline.co.uk/flight/dursley.html
  Includes some inscriptions for Cam, Dursley and Uley

- Some Memorial Inscriptions: Dursley, Gloucestershire. St. James's Churchyard
  www.wishful-thinking.org.uk/genuki/GLS/Dursley/MIs.html

Eastington
- Some Memorial Inscriptions: Eastington (nr. Stonehouse), Gloucestershire: St. Michael & All Angels Churchyard
  www.wishful-thinking.org.uk/genuki/GLS/EastingtonStonehouse/MIs.html

Elburton
- Some Memorial Inscriptions: Elberton, Gloucestershire: St. John's Churchyard
  www.wishful-thinking.org.uk/genuki/GLS/Elberton/MIs.html

Falfield
- Some Memorial Inscriptions: Falfield, Gloucestershire: St. George's Churchyard
  www.wishful-thinking.org.uk/genuki/GLS/Falfield/MIs.html

Frampton on Severn
- Some Memorial Inscriptions: Frampton on Severn, Gloucestershire:
  www.wishful-thinking.org.uk/genuki/GLS/FramaptononSevern/MIs.html

Fretherne
- Some Memorial Inscriptions: Fretherne, Gloucestershire: St. Mary the Virgin's Churchyard
  www.wishful-thinking.org.uk/genuki/GLS/Fretherne/MIs.html

Frocester
- Some Memorial Inscriptions: Frocester, Gloucestershire: St. Peter's Priory Churchyard
  www.wishful-thinking.org.uk/genuki/GLS/Frocester/MIs.html

Hardwicke
- Some Memorial Inscriptions: Hardwicke, Gloucestershire. St. Nicholas Churchyard
  www.wishful-thinking.org.uk/genuki/GLS/Hardwicke/MIs.html

Harescombe
- Harescombe, Gloucestershire: Monumental Inscriptions 1880
  web.ukonline.co.uk/flight/harescombe.html
  Notes from *Gloucestershire Notes & Queries* **1**, 1881.

Hawkesbury
- Some Memorial Inscriptions: Hawkesbury, Gloucestershire. St. Mary the Virgin Churchyard and Cemetery
  www.wishful-thinking.org.uk/genuki/GLS/Hawkesbury/MIs.html

Hempsted
- Hempsted Church: Monumental Inscriptions
  web.ukonline.co.uk/flight/hempstedmi.html

Hill
- Some Memorial Inscriptions, Hill, Gloucestershire: St. Michael the Archangel's Churchyard
  www.wishful-thinking.org.uk/genuki/GLS/Hill/MIs.html

Horsley

- Some Memorial Inscriptions: Horsley, Gloucestershire: St. Martin's Churchyard
  www.wishful-thinking.org.uk/genuki/GLS/Horsley/Mls.html

King's Stanley

- Some Memorial Inscriptions: King's Stanley, Gloucestershire. St. George's Churchyard and Selsley United Church
  www.wishful-thinking.org.uk/genuki/GLS/KingsStanley/Mls.html

- St. George's Church, King's Stanley: Monumental Inscriptions
  www.grahamthomas.com/KingStanMem.html

- St. George's Church, King's Stanley, Gloucestershire: Monumental Inscriptions
  web.ukonline.co.uk/flight/stanley/ksdeaths.html
  From *Gloucestershire Notes & Queries* 1881

Kingswood

- Some Memorial Inscriptions: Kingswood (nr. Wotton) Gloucestershire, St. Mary's Churchyard and Cemetery
  www.wishful-thinking.org.uk/genuki/GLS/KingswoodWilts/Mls.html

Leckhampton

- St. Philip & St. James Church: Monumental Inscriptions
  www.ukonline.co.uk/flight/cheltenham/cheltstpstjmi.html
  Leckhampton; from *Gloucestershire Notes & Queries* 1881

Leighterton

- Some Memorial Inscriptions: Leighterton, Gloucestershire: St. Andrew's Churchyard
  www.wishful-thinking.org.uk/genuki/GLS/Leighterton/Mls.html

Leonard Stanley

- Some Memorial Inscriptions: Leonard Stanley, Gloucestershire: St. Swithin's Churchyard
  www.wishful-thinking.org.uk/genuki/GLS/LeonardStanley/Mls.html

Littleton on Severn

- Some Memorial Inscriptions: Littleton on Severn, Gloucestershire: St. Mary's Churchyard
  www.wishful-thinking.org.uk/genuki/GLS/LittletononSevern/Mls.html

Long Newnton

- Some Memorial Inscriptions: Long Newnton, Gloucestershire. Holy Trinity Churchyard
  www.wishful-thinking.org.uk/genuki/GLS/LongNewnton/Mls.html

- Holy Trinity, Long Newnton, Gloucestershire
  www.oodwooc.f9.co.uk/ph__longnewn.htm
  Photographs of inscriptions

Longney

- Longney, Gloucestershire, UK Church Memorial Inscriptions 1879
  web.ukonline.co.uk/flight/longneymi.html
  Recorded in 1879, and published in *Gloucestershire Notes & Queries* 1881

Minchinhampton

- Some Memorial Inscriptions: Minchinhampton, Gloucestershire. Holy Trinity Churchyard
  www.wishful-thinking.org.uk/genuki/GLS/Minchinhampton/Mls.html

Miserden

- Miserden, Gloucestershire, England
  web.ukonline.co.uk/flight/miserden.html
  Monumental inscriptions from *Gloucestershire Notes & Queries,* 1881, and war memorial

Moreton Valence

- Some Memorial Inscriptions: Moreton Valence, Gloucestershire. St. Stephen's Churchyard
  www.wishful-thinking.org.uk/genuki/GLS/MoretonValence/Mls.html

Nailsworth

- Some Memorial Inscriptions: Nailsworth, Gloucestershire: Baptist Church, Rockhill
  www.wishful-thinking.org.uk/genuki/GLS/Nailsworth/Mls.html

Newland

- Some Memorial Inscriptions: Newland, Gloucestershire: All Saints Churchyard
  www.wishful-thinking.org.uk/genuki/GLS/Newland/Mls.html

Newport

- Some Memorial Inscriptions: Newport, Gloucestershire. Newport Independent Chapel
  www.wishful-thinking.org.uk/genuki/GLS/Newport/Mls.html

North Nibley

- Monumental Inscriptions in North Nibley
www.genuki.org.uk/big/eng/GLS/NorthNibley/Mls.html

- Some Memorial Inscriptions: North Nibley, Gloucestershire. St. Martin's Churchyard and Cemetery
www.wishful-thinking.org.uk/genuki/GLS/NorthNibley/Mls.html

Northwick

- Some Memorial Inscriptions: Northwick, Gloucestershire. St. Thomas Church Tower
www.wishful-thinking.org.uk/genuki/GLS/Northwick/Mls.html

Nympsfield

- Some Memorial Inscriptions: Nympsfield, Gloucestershire: St. Bartholomew's Churchyard
www.wishful-thinking.org.uk/genuki/GLS/Nympsfield/Mls.html

Oakridge

- Some Memorial Inscriptions: Oakridge, Gloucestershire. Methodist Churchyard
www.wishful-thinking.org.uk/genuki/GLS/Oakridge/Mls.html

Oldbury on Severn

- Some Memorial Inscriptions: Oldbury on Severn, Gloucestershire: St. Arilda's Churchyard and Cemetery
www.wishful-thinking.org.uk/genuki/GLS/OldburyonSevern/Mls.html

Olveston

- Some Memorial Inscriptions: Olveston, Gloucestershire. St. Mary's Churchyard
www.wishful-thinking.org.uk/genuki/GLS/Olveston/Mls.html

Ozleworth

- Some Memorial Inscriptions: Ozleworth, Gloucestershire: St. Nicholas of Myra's Churchyard
www.wishful-thinking.org.uk/genuki/GLS/Ozleworth/Mls.html

Painswick

- St. Mary's Church, Painswick, Monumental Inscriptions
web.ukonline.co.uk/flight/painmem.html

Pitchcombe

- Pitchcombe, Gloucestershire, England
www.geocities.com/Heartland/Ranch/8066/pitchcom.html
Monumental Inscriptions extracted from *Gloucestershire notes & queries,* 1881

- Some Memorial Inscriptions: Pitchcombe, Gloucestershire: St. John the Baptist's Churchyard
www.wishful-thinking.org.uk/genuki/GLS/Pitchcombe.html

Prestbury

- Prestbury, Gloucestershire: Monumental Inscriptions
web.ukonline.co.uk/flight/prestburymi.html
Extracted from *Gloucestershire notes & queries,* 1881

Randwick

- Bigland's Memorial Inscriptions, Randwick
www.sandford.plus.com/Randwick/Bigland/Bigland__Contents.html
Extracted from BIGLAND, RALPH. *Historical monumental and genealogical collections relative to the County of Gloucester.* 1792.

- Randwick, Gloucestershire
web.ukonline.co.uk/flight/randwick.html
Includes monumental inscriptions, and war memorial

- Some Memorial Inscriptions: Randwick, Gloucestershire: St. John the Baptist's Churchyard
www.wishful-thinking.org.uk/genuki/GLS/Randwick/Mls.html

Rangeworthy

- Some Memorial Inscriptions: Rangeworthy, Gloucestershire: Holy Trinity Churchyard and Cemetery
www.wishful-thinking.org.uk/genuki/GLS/Rangeworthy/Mls.html

Rockhampton

- Some Memorial Inscriptions: Rockhampton, Gloucestershire. St. Oswald's Churchyard
www.wishful-thinking.org.uk/genuki/GLS/Rockhampton/Mls.html

Rodborough

- Rodborough Church Monumental Inscriptions
www.grahamthomas.com/Rodmem.html
Originally published in *Gloucestershire notes & queries,* 1881

- Rodborough, Gloucestershire Monumental Inscriptions
  web.ukonline.co.uk/flight/roddeath.html
  Extracted from *Gloucestershire notes & queries,* 1881

- Some Memorial Inscriptions: Rodborough, Gloucestershire: St. Mary Magdalene's Churchyard
  www.wishful-thinking.org.uk/genuki/GLS/Rodborough/MIs.html

Rodmarton

- Some Memorial Inscriptions: Rodmarton, Gloucestershire: St. Peter's Churchyard
  www.wishful-thinking.org.uk/genuki/GLS/Rodmarton/MIs.html

Ruardean

- Some Memorial Inscriptions: Ruardean, Gloucestershire: St. John's Churchyard
  www.wishful-thinking.org.uk/genuki/GLS/Ruardean/MIs.html

Sapperton

- Some Memorial Inscriptions: Sapperton, Gloucestershire. St. Kenelm's Churchyard
  www.wishful-thinking.org.uk/genuki/GLS/Sapperton/MIs.html

Saul

- Some Memorial Inscriptions: Saul, Gloucestershire: St. James' Churchyard
  www.wishful-thinking.org.uk/genuki/GLS/Saul/MIs.html

Selsley

- Some Memorial Inscriptions: Selsley, Gloucestershire. All Saints Churchyard
  www.wishful-thinking.org.uk/genuki/GLS/Selsley/MIs.html

Slimbridge

- Some Memorial Inscriptions: Slimbridge, Gloucestershire: St. John the Evangelist's Churchyard
  www.wishful-thinking.org.uk/genuki/GLS/Slimbridge/MIs.html

Standish

- Some Memorial Inscriptions: Standish, Gloucestershire: St. Nicholas's Churchyard
  www.wishful-thinking.org.uk/genuki/GLS/Standish/MIs.html

Stinchcombe

- Some Memorial Inscriptions: Stinchcombe, Gloucestershire: St. Cyr's Churchyard
  www.wishful-thinking.org.uk/genuki/GLS/Stinchcombe/MIs.html

Stone

- Some Memorial Inscriptions: Stone, Gloucestershire. All Saints Churchyard
  www.wishful-thinking.org.uk/genuki/GLS/Stone/MIs.html

Stonehouse

- Stonehouse, Gloucestershire: Monumental Inscriptions
  web.ukonline.co.uk/flight/stonehouse.html
  Extracted mainly from *Gloucestershire notes & queries* 1881

- Some Memorial Inscriptions: Stonehouse, Gloucestershire: St. Cyr's Churchyard and Cemetery
  www.wishful-thinking.org.uk/genuki/GLS/Stonehouse/MIs.html

Stratton

- St. Peter's, Stratton, Gloucestershire
  www.oodwooc.f9.co.uk/ph__strattonG.htm
  Photographs of inscriptions

Stroud

- Stroud, Gloucestershire: Monumental Inscriptions
  web.ukonline.co.uk/flight/stroudmi.html

Swindon

- Swindon, nr. Cheltenham: Monumental Inscriptions
  web.ukonline.co.uk/flight/swindonmi.html
  Extracted from *Gloucestershire notes & queries,* 1881 and *The Genealogist,* 1877-9
  rB
  >ury

- Some Memorial Inscriptions: Tetbury, Gloucestershire: St. Mary the Virgin and St. Saviour's Churchyard
  www.wishful-thinking.org.uk/genuki/GLS/Tetbury/MIs.html

- Tetbury, Gloucestershire: Monumental Inscriptions
  web.ukonline.co.uk/flight/tetburymi.html
  Recorded in 1857

Thornbury

- Some Memorial Inscriptions: Thornbury. Gloucestershire. St. Mary the Virgin Churchyard and Kington Cemetery
  www.wishful-thinking.org.uk/genuki/GLS/Thornbury/MIs.html

Tortworth

- Some Memorial Inscriptions: Tortworth, Gloucestershire: St. Leonard's Churchyard
  www.wishful-thinking.org.uk/genuki/GLS/Tortworth/MIs.html

Tresham

- Some Memorial Inscriptions: Tresham, Gloucestershire. Churchyard
  www.wishful-thinking.org.uk/genuki/GLS/Tresham/MIs.html

Tytherington

- Some Memorial Inscriptions: Tytherington, Gloucestershire. St. James' Churchyard
  www.wishful-thinking.org.uk/genuki/GLS/Tytherington/MIs.html

Uley

See also Dursley

- Some Memorial Inscriptions: Uley, Gloucestershire: St. Giles' Churchyard
  www.wishful-thinking.org.uk/genuki/GLS/Uley/MIs.html

Welford on Avon

- Monumental Inscriptions for Welford on Avon, St. Peter
  www.hunimex.com/warwick/mi/mi__welford.html
  List of surnames on fiche no. 1249, available from the Birmingham and Midland Society for Genealogy & Heraldry.

Wickwar

- Some Memorial Inscriptions: Wickwar, Gloucestershire: Holy Trinity Churchyard and Cemetery
  www.wishful-thinking.org.uk/genuki/GLS/Wickwar/MIs.html

Woodchester

- Some Memorial Inscriptions: Woodchester, Gloucestershire: St. Mary's Churchyard and Ruins of Old Church
  www.wishful-thinking.org.uk/genuki/GLS/Woodchester/MIs.html

- Woodchester, Gloucestershire Monumental Inscriptions
  web.ukonline.co.uk/flight/woodchester.html
  Extracted from *Gloucestershire notes & queries,* 1881

Wotton under Edge

- Some Memorial Inscriptions, Wotton under Edge, Gloucestershire St. Mary's Churchyard and Cemetery
  www.wishful-thinking.org.uk/genuki/GLS/WottonunderEdge/MIs.html

Yate

- Some Memorial Inscriptions: Yate, Gloucestershire: St. Mary's Churchyard
  www.wishful-thinking.org.uk/genuki/GLS/Yate/MIs.html

Hampshire

Institutional Collections
- Monumental Inscriptions
  **www.iow.gov.uk/library/record__office/Types__of__Records/
  monument.asp**
  Transcripts held by the Isle of Wight Record Offices

Indexes
- North East Hampshire Monumental Inscription Index
  website.lineone.net/~hantshistory/ne-mi-intro.html
  Index to 32 churchyards

- Monumental Inscriptions: Hampshire
  www.towball.freewire.co.uk/hampshire.htm
  Index. Mainly from Old Basing, Warblington and South Hayling

Publications
- Hampshire Genealogical Society Publications: Monumental Inscriptions
  www.hgs-online.org.uk/hgs__pub__mi.htm
  List of fiche

Brasses
- Monumental Brass Rubbings for England: Hampshire
  www.ashmol.co.uk/ash/departments/antiquities/brass.htm
  Click on 'Catalogue' and county. In the Ashmolean Museum, Oxford

- Hampshire (Including Isle of Wight)
  www.mbs-brasses.co.uk/Hampshire.htm
  Bibliography of monumental brasses

East Meon
- East Meon Gravestones and other memorials
  www.safari.freeserve.co.uk/memorials.htm

- East Meon Gravestones & other Memorials
  www.parishregisters.co.uk
  Click on 'Hampshire', 'East Meon', and 'Memorials List'. Also at
  **freepages.genealogy.rootsweb.com/~parishregisters/hampshire/
  eastmeon/memorials.htm**

Froyle
- Monumental Inscriptions at St. Mary of the Assumption, Froyle, Hampshire
  website.lineone.net/~hantshistory/mi-froyle-4.html

Hamble
- St. Andrew's Church, Hamble: Cemetery Records
  uk.geocities.com/theon1940/

Hawley
- The History of the 'old' All Saints Church, Hawley
  www.hawleygreen.org.uk/all__saints__history.htm
  Includes inscriptions

Headley
- Monumental Inscriptions in Headley: Introduction
  my.genie.co.uk/headleyvillage/mi/intro.htm

- Monumental Inscriptions in Headley: Burials in All Saints' Churchyard
  my.genie.co.uk/headleyvillage/mi/mi.htm

Long Sutton
- Long Sutton, Hampshire: Church & Churchyard Monumental Inscriptions: list of surnames
  website.lineone.net/~hantshistory/mi-ls.html

Old Basing
- Inscriptions from Old Basing, Hampshire
  www.towball.freewire.co.uk/inscri19.htm

South Hayling
- Inscriptions from St. Mary's & St. Peter's, South Hayling, Hampshire
  www.towball.freewire.co.uk/inscr8.htm

Southampton
- Cemetery Information
  **www.southampton.gov.uk/government/environment/environhlth/
  bercemeteryinfo.htm**

  For Southampton

Warblington
- Inscriptions from St. Thomas a Becket, Warblington
  www.towball.freewire.co.uk/inscr11.htm
  Selected inscriptions

Herefordshire

Indexes
- Herefordshire Family History Society Monumental Inscriptions
  www.rootsweb.com/~ukhfhs/miindex.html
  On-line index to published fiche

Brasses
- Monumental Brass Rubbings for England: Herefordshire
  www.ashmol.co.uk/ash/departments/antiquities/brass/
  Click on 'Catalogue' and county. In the Ashmolean Museum, Oxford.

- Herefordshire
  www.mbs-brasses.co.uk/Herefordshire.htm
  Bibliography of monumental brasses

Publications
- Herefordshire Family History Society: Publications
  www.rootsweb.com/~ukhfhs/pubs.html
  Includes many monumental inscriptions on fiche

Birley
- Herefordshire: St. Peter, Birley Monumental Inscriptions
  www.genuki.org.uk/big/eng/HEF/Birley/mibirley.html

Dilwyn
- Herefordshire: St. Mary, Dilwyn Monumental Inscriptions
  www.genuki.org.uk/big/eng/HEF/Dilwyn/midilwyn.html

Donnington
- Some Memorial Inscriptions: Donnington, Herefordshire, St. Mary's
  Church and Churchyard
  www.wishful-thinking.org.uk/genuki/HEF/Donnington/MI's.html

Monkland
- Herefordshire: All Saints, Monkland Monumental Inscriptions
  www.genuki.org.uk/big/eng/HEF/Monkland/mimonkld.html

Norton Canon
- Herefordshire: St. Nicholas, Norton Cannon Monumental Inscriptions
  www.genuki.org.uk/big/eng/HEF/Norton Canon/minrtcan.html

Sarnesfield
- Herefordshire: St. Mary, Sarnesfield Monumental Inscriptions
www.genuki.org.uk/big/eng/HEF/Sarnesfield/misarnsf.html

Titley
- Some Memorial Inscriptions: Titley, Herefordshire. St. Peter's Church
www.wishful-thinking.org.uk/genuki/HEF/Titley/Mls.html

Hertfordshire

Indexes
- Monumental Inscriptions: Hertfordshire
www.towball.freewire.co.uk/hertfordshire.htm
Index. All from Ardeley at present, but more may be added.

Brasses
- Monumental Brass Rubbings for England: Hertfordshire
www.ashmole.co.uk/ash/departments/antiquities/brass/
Click on 'Catalogue' and county. In the Ashmolean Museum, Oxford

- Hertfordshire
www.mbs-brasses.co.uk/Hertfordshire.htm
Bibliography of monumental brasses

Publications
- Hertfordshire Family & Population History Society: Major Publications: Monumental Inscriptions
www.hertsfhs.org.uk/hfphs30.html

Ardeley
- Inscriptions from Hertfordshire churches
www.towball.freewire.co.uk/inscr__4.htm
Selected Ardeley inscriptions

Huntingdonshire

Brasses
- Monumental Brass Rubbings for England: Huntingdonshire
  www.ashmol.co.uk/ash/departments/antiquities/brass/
  Click on 'Catalogue' and county. In the Ashmolean Museum, Oxford

- Huntingdonshire
  www.mbs-brasses.co.uk/Huntingdonshire.htm
  Bibliography of monumental brasses

Isle of Man

General
- Memorials of 'God's Acre', being Monumental Inscriptions in the Isle of Man taken in the summer of 1797 by John Feltham and Edward Wright
  www.isle-of-man.com/manxnotebook/manxsoc/msvol14/index.htm

Publications
- Isle of Man Family History Society Publications
  www.isle-of-man.com/interests/genealogy/fhs/fhspub.shtml
  Includes monumental inscriptions, burial registers *etc.*

Kent

General

- D'Elboux Manuscripts: Indexed Abstracts
  users.iclway.co.uk/barrywhite/Kent/pk__delbo1.pdf
  Extracts from monumental inscriptions for Kent. Continued at
  /pk__delbo2.pdf and **/pk__delbo3.pdf**

Indexes

- Monumental Inscriptions: Kent
  www.towball.freewire.co.uk/Kent.htm
  Index. Under construction

Brasses

- Monumental Brass Rubbings for England: Kent
  www.ashmol.co.uk/ash/departments/antiquities/brass/
  Click on 'Catalogue' and county. In the Ashmolean Museum, Oxford

- Kent
  www.mbs-brasses.co.uk/Kent.htm
  Bibliography of monumental brasses

Acrise

- Acrise
  www.kentarchaeology.org.uk/Research/Libr/Mls/MlAcrise/01.htm
  Monumental inscriptions recorded in 1891

Alkham

- Alkham
  www.kentarchaeology.org.uk/Research/Libr/Mls/MlsAlkham/01.htm

Ash cum Ridley

- Ash-cum-Ridley
  www.kentarchaeology.org.uk/Research/Libr/Mls/MlsAsh-cum-Ridley.htm
  Monumental inscriptions recorded in 1889

Bethersden

- Bethersden
  **www.kentarchaeology.org.uk/Research/Libr/Mls/MlsBethersden/
  MlsBethersden.htm**
  Monumental inscriptions, recorded c.100 years ago

Biddenden

- Biddenden
  **www.kentarchaeology.org.uk/Research/Libr/Mls/MlsBiddenden/
  MlsBiddenden.htm**
  Monumental inscriptions, recorded c.100 years ago

Boughton Aluph

- Boughton Aluph
  www.kentarchaeology.org.uk/Research/Libr/Mls/MlsBoughton%20Aluph/01.htm
  Monumental inscriptions, recorded in 1890

Brabourne

- Brabourne
  www.kentarchaeology.org.uk/Research/Libr/Mls/MlsBrabourne/01.htm
  Monumental inscriptions, recorded 1890

Brenzett

- Brenzett
  www.kentarchaeology.org.uk/Research/Libr/Mls/MlsBrenzett/01.htm
  Monumental inscriptions, recorded c.100 years ago

Brook

- Brook
  www.kentarchaeology.org.uk/Research/Libr/Mls/MlsBrook/01.htm
  Monumental inscriptions, recorded c.100 years ago

Brookland

- Brookland
  www.kentarchaeology.org.uk/Research/Libr/Mls/MlsBrookland/01.htm
  Monumental inscriptions, recorded c.100 years ago

Burmarsh

- Burmarsh
  www.kentarchaeology.org.uk/Research/Libr/Mls/MlsBurmarsh/01.htm
  Monumental inscriptions, recorded c.100 years ago

Capel

- Capel near Tonbridge
  www.kentarchaeology.org.uk/Research/Libr/Ml's/MlsCapelnrTonbridge/01.htm

Capel le Ferne

- Capel le Ferne
  www.kentarchaeology.org.uk/Research/Libr/Mls/MlsCapel-le-Ferne.htm
  Monumental inscriptions recorded in 1891

Charing

- Charing
  www.kentarchaeology.org.uk/Research/Libr/Mls/MlsCharing/01.htm
  Monumental inscriptions, recorded in 1920

Chelsfield

- Chelsfield
  www.kentarchaeology.org.uk/Research/Libr/Mls/MlsChelsfield/
  MlsChelsfield.htm

  Monumental inscriptions, recorded in 1890

Cheriton

- Cheriton
  www.kentarchaeology.org.uk/Research/Libr/MlsCheriton/01.htm
  Monumental inscriptions recorded in 1891

Darenth

- Darenth
  www.kentarchaeology.org.uk/Research/Libr/Mls/MlsDarenth/
  MlsDarenth.htm

  Monumental inscriptions, recorded in 1920

Dartford

- Dartford
  www.kentarchaeology.org.uk/Research/Libr/Mls/MlsDartford/
  MlsDartford.htm

  Monumental inscriptions, recorded in 1877

Deptford

- Deptford
  www.kentarchaeology.org.uk/Research/Libr/Mls/MlsDeptford/
  MlsDeptford.htm

  Monumental inscriptions, recorded in the 1870s

Downe

- Downe
  www.kentarchaeology.org.uk/Research/Libr/Mls/MlsDowne/
  MlsDowne.htm

  Monumental inscriptions, recorded in 1919

Dymchurch

- Dymchurch
  www.kentarchaeology.org.uk/Research/Libr/Mls/MlsDymchurch/
  MlsDymchurch.htm

  Monumental inscriptions, recorded c.100 years ago

East Peckham

- East Peckham
  www.kentarchaeology.org.uk/Research/Libr/Mls/MlsEast%20Peckham/01.htm

Ebony

- Ebony, Isle of Oxney
  www.kentarchaeology.org.uk/Research/Libr/Mls/MlsEbony/01.htm
  Forthcoming. Monumental inscriptions, recorded in 1919

Egerton

- Egerton
  www.kentarchaeology.org.uk/Research/Libr/Mls/MlsEgerton/01.htm
  Monumental inscriptions, recorded c.100 years ago

Elham

- Elham
  www.kentarchaeology.org.uk/Research/Libr/Mls/MlsElham/01.htm
  Monumental inscriptions recorded in 1891

Elmstead

- Elmstead
  www.kentarchaeology.org.uk/Research/Libr/Mls/MlsElmstead/01.htm
  Monumental inscriptions, recorded c.100 years ago

Fairfield

- Fairfield
  www.kentarchaeology.org.uk/Research/Libr/Mls/MlsFairfield/01.htm
  Monumental inscriptions, recorded c.100 years ago

Fawkham

- Fawkham
  www.kentarchaeology.org.uk/Research/Libr/Mls/MlsFawkham/MlsFawkham.htm
  Monumental inscriptions, recorded in 1890

Folkestone

- Folkestone
  www.kentarchaeology.org.uk/Research/Libr/Mls/MlFolkestone/01.htm
  Monumental inscriptions recorded in 1891

Footscray

- Footscray
  www.kentarchaeology.org.uk/Research/Libr/Mls/MlsFootscray/
  MlsFootscray.htm
  Monumental inscriptions, recorded c.100 years ago

Godmersham

- Godmersham
  www.kentarchaeology.org.uk/Research/Libr/Mls/MlsGodmersham/01.htm
  Monumental inscriptions recorded in 1890

Goudhurst

- Goudhurst
  www.kentarchaeology.org.uk/Research/Libr/Mls/Mlslist.htm
  Forthcoming. Monumental inscriptions, recorded c.100 years ago

Hartley

- Hartley
  www.kentarchaeology.org.uk/Research/Libr.Mls/MlsHartley/
  MlsHartley.htm
  Monumental inscriptions, recorded in 1890

Hastingley

- Hastingleigh
  www.kentarchaeology.org.uk/Research/Libr/Mls/MlsHastingleigh/01.htm
  Monumental inscriptions, recorded in 1890

Hawkhurst

- Hawkhurst
  www.kentarchaeology.org.uk/Research/Libr/Mls/Mlslist.htm
  Forthcoming. Monumental inscriptions, recorded c.100 years ago

Hawkinge

- Hawkinge
  www.kentarchaeology.org.uk/Research/Libr/Mls/MlHawkinge/01.htm
  Monumental inscriptions recorded in 1891

Headcorn

- Headcorn
  www.kentarchaeology.org.uk/Research/Libr/Mls/MlsHeadcorn/
  MlsHeadcorn.htm
  Monumental inscriptions, recorded in 1923

High Halden

- High Halden
  www.kentarchaeology.org.uk/Research/Libr/Mls/MlsHighHalden/
  High%20Halden%20Churchyard%20M__l-'s.htm
  Monumental inscriptions, recorded in 1894

Hinxhill

- Hinxhill
  www.kentarchaeology.org.uk/Research/Libr/Mls/MlsHinxhill/01.htm
  Monumental inscriptions, recorded in 1890

Horsmonden

- Horsmonden
  www.kentarchaeology.org.uk/Research/Libr/Mls/Mlslist.htm
  Forthcoming. Monumental inscriptions, recorded c.100 years ago

Horton Kirby

- Horton Kirby
  www.kentarchaeology.org.uk/Research/Libr/Mls/MlsHortonKirby/
  MlsHortonKirby.htm
  Monumental inscriptions recorded in 1889-90

Hothfield

- Hothfield
  www.kentarchaeology.org.uk/Research/Libr/Mlslist.htm
  Forthcoming. Monumental inscriptions, recorded c.100 years ago

Hougham

- Hougham
  www.kentarchaeology.org.uk/Research/Libr/Mls/MlsHougham/01.htm
  Monumental inscriptions recorded in 1891

Hunton

- Hunton
  www.kentarchaeology.org.uk/Research/Libr/Mlslist.htm
  Forthcoming. Monumental inscriptions, recorded c.100 years ago

Hythe

- Hythe
  www.kentarchaeology.org.uk/Research/Libr/Mls/MlsHythe/01.htm
  Monumental inscriptions recorded in 1891

Ifield

- Ifield
  www.kentarchaeology.org.uk/Research/Libr/Mls/MlsIfield/MlsIfield.htm
  Monumental inscriptions, recorded c.100 years ago

Ivychurch

- Ivychurch
  www.kentarchaeology.org.uk/Research/Libr/Mls/MlsIvychurch/01.htm
  Monumental inscriptions, recorded c.100 years ago

Kemsing

- Kemsing
  www.kentarchaeology.org.uk/Research/Libr/Mls/MlsKemsing/MlsKemsing.htm
  Monumental inscriptions, recorded in 1921

Kennardington

- Kennardington
  www.kentarchaeology.org.uk/Research/Libr/Mls/Mlslist.htm
  Forthcoming. Monumental inscriptions, recorded c.100 years ago

Kennington

- Kennington
  www.kentarchaeology.org.uk/Research/Libr/Mls/MlsKennington/01.htm
  Monumental inscriptions recorded in 1890

Keston

- Keston
  www.kentarchaeology.org.uk/Research/Libr/Mls/MlsKeston/MlsKeston.htm
  Monumental inscriptions, recorded in 1891

Kingsdown

- Kingsdown (West)
  www.kentarchaeology.org.uk/Research/Libr/Mls/MlsWestKingsdown/MlsKingsdown%20(West).htm
  Monumental inscriptions, recorded in 1890

Knockholt

- Knockholt
  www.kentarchaeology.org.uk/Research/Libr/Mls/MlsKnockholt/MlsKnockholt.htm
  Monumental inscriptions, recorded in 1891

Lamberhurst

- Lamberhurst
  www.kentarchaeoogy.org.uk/Research/Libr/Mls/MlsLamberhurst/MlsLamberhurst.htm
  Monumental inscriptions, recorded in 1923

Lee

- Lee
  www.kentarchaeology.org.uk/Research/Libr/Mls/MlLee/MlsLee.htm
  Monumental inscriptions, recorded in 1830

Lewisham

- Lewisham
  www.kentarchaeology.org.uk/Research/Libr/Mls/Mlslist.htm
  Forthcoming. Monumental inscriptions, recorded c.100 years ago

Little Chart

- Little Chart
  www.kentarchaeology.org.uk/Research/Libr/Mls/MlsLittleChart/01.htm
  Monumental inscriptions, recorded in 1920

Longfield

- Longfield
  www.kentarchaeology.org.uk/Research/Libr/Mls/MlsLongfield/MlsLongfield.htm
  Monumental inscriptions, recorded in 1890

Lydd

- Lydd
  www.kentarchaeology.org.uk/Research/Libr/Mls/MlsLydd/MlsLydd.htm
  Monumental inscriptions recorded in a book published in 1927

Lyminge

- Lyminge
  www.kentarchaeology.org.uk/Research/Libr/Mls/MlsLyminge/01.htm
  Monumental inscription recorded in 1891

Maidstone

- Memorial Inscriptions at All Saints, Maidstone: Surname List
  freepages.genealogy.rootsweb.com/~mrawson/maids-mi.html
  Surnames only

New Romney
- New Romney
  www.kentarchaeology.org.uk/Research/Libr/Mls/Mlslist.htm
  Forthcoming. Monumental inscriptions, recorded c.100 years ago

Newchurch
- Newchurch
  www.kentarchaeology.org.uk/Research/Libr/Mls/Mlslist.htm
  Forthcoming. Monumental inscriptions, recorded c.100 years ago

Newenden
- Newenden
  www.kentarchaeology.org.uk/Research/Libr/Mls/MlsNewenden/01.htm
  Monumental inscriptions, recorded in 1917

Newington
- Newington
  www.kentarchaeology.org.uk/Research/Libr/Mls/MlsNewington/ MlsNewington.htm
  Monumental inscriptions, recorded late 19th c.

North Cray
- North Cray
  www.kentarchaeology.org.uk/Research/Libr/Mls/MlsNorthCray/ MlsNorthCray.htm
  Monumental inscriptions, recorded in 1920

Nurstead
- Nursted
  www.kentarchaeology.org.uk/Research/Libr/Mls/MlsNursted/ MlsNursted.htm
  Monumental inscriptions, recorded c.100 years ago

Old Romney
- Old Romney
  www.kentarchaeology.org.uk/Research/Libr/Mls/MlsOldRomney/01.htm
  Monumental inscriptions, recorded c.100 years ago

Orlestone
- Orlestone
  www.kentarchaeology.org.uk/Research/Libr/Mls/MlsOrlestone/01.htm
  Monumental inscriptions, recorded c.100 years ago

Orpington
- Orpington
  www.kentarchaeology.org.uk/Research/Libr/Mls/MlsOrpington/ MlsOrpington.htm
  Monumental inscriptions, recorded c.100 years ago

Paddlesworth
- Paddlesworth
  www.kentarchaeology.org.uk/Research/Libr/Mls/MlsPaddlesworth/01.htm
  Monumental inscriptions, recorded in 1891

Pluckley
- Pluckley
  www.kentarchaeology.org.uk/Research/Libr/Mls/Mlslist.htm
  Forthcoming. Monumental inscriptions, recorded c.100 years ago

Postling
- Postling
  www.kentarchaeology.org.uk/Research/Libr/Mls/MlsPostling/01.htm
  Monumental inscriptions recorded in 1891

Ridley
- Ridley
  www.kentarchaeology.org.uk/Research/Libr/Mls/MlsRidley/MlsRidley.htm
  Monumental inscriptions, recorded in 1890

Rolvenden
- Rolvenden
  www.kentarchaeology.org.uk/Research/Libr/Mls/Mlslist.htm
  Forthcoming. Monumental inscriptions, recorded c.100 years ago

St. Mary Cray
- St. Mary Cray
  www.kentarchaeology.org.uk/Research/Libr/Mls/MlsStMaryCray/ MlsStMaryCray.htm
  Monumental inscriptions, recorded in 1921

St. Mary in the Marsh
- St. Mary-in-the-Marsh
  www.kentarchaeology.org.uk/Research/Libr/Mls/ MlsStMary-in-the-Marsh/MlsStMary-in-the-Marsh.htm
  Monumental inscriptions, recorded c.100 years ago

St. Paul Cray
- St. Paul Cray
www.kentarchaeology.org.uk/Research/Libr/Mls/MlsStPaulCray/
MlsStPaulCray.htm

  Monumental inscriptions, recorded in 1920

Shipbourne
- Shipbourne
www.kentarchaeology.org.uk/Research/Libr/Mls/MlsShipbourne/
MlsShipbourne.htm

  Monumental inscriptions, recorded in 1923

Shoreham
- Shoreham
www.kentarchaeology.org.uk/Research/Libr/Mls/MlsShoreham/
MlsShoreham.htm

  Monumental inscriptions, recorded c.1919

Snargate
- Snargate
www.kentarchaeology.org.uk/Research/Libr/Mls/MlsSnargate/01.htm
Monumental inscriptions, recorded c.100 years ago

Snave
- Snave
www.kentarchaeology.org.uk/Research/Libr/Mls/MlsSnave/01.htm
Monumental inscriptions recorded c.100 years ago

Southfleet
- Southfleet
www.kentarchaeology.org.uk/Research/Libr/Mls/MlsSouthfleet/
MlsSouthfleet.htm

  Monumental inscriptions, recorded in 1922

Stalisfield
- Stalisfield
www.kentarchaeology.org.uk/Research/Libr/Mls/MlsStalisfield/
MlsStalisfield.htm

  Monumental inscriptions, recorded in 1920

Stanford
- Stanford
www.kentarchaeology.org.uk/Research/Libr/Mls/MlsStanford/01.htm
Monumental inscriptions recorded in 1891

Tenterden
- Tenterden
www.kentarchaeology.org.uk/Research/Libr/Mls/MlsTenterden/
MlsTenterden.htm

  Monumental inscriptions, from a book published in 1919

Thanet
- D'Elboux Manuscripts: extracts relating to Thanet
users.iclway.co.uk/barrywhite/people/pt__delbo.pdf
Monumental inscriptions

Warehorne
- Warehorne
www.kentarchaeology.org.uk/Research/Libr/Mls/MlsWarehorne/01.htm
Monumental inscriptions, recorded c.100 years ago

Westwell
- Westwell
www.kentarchaeology.org.uk/Research/Libr/Mls/MlsWestwell/
MlsWestwell.htm

  Monumental inscriptions, recorded in 1920

West Wickham
- West Wickham
www.kentarchaeology.org.uk/Research/Libr/Mls/MlsWestWickham/
MlsWestWickham.htm

  Monumental inscriptions, recorded in 1891

Wilmington
- Wilmington
www.kentarchaeology.org.uk/Research/Libr/Mls/MlsWilmington/
MlsWilmington.htm

  Monumental inscriptions, recorded in 1921

Woolwich

- Woolwich
  www.kentarchaeology.org.uk/Research/Libr/Mls/Mlslist.htm
  Forthcoming. Monumental inscriptions, recorded c.100 years ago

Wrotham

- Wrotham
  www.kentarchaeology.org.uk/Research/Libr/Mls/MlsWrotham/
  MlsWrotham.htm
  Monumental inscriptions, recorded c.1919

Wye

- Wye
  www.kentarchaeology.org.uk/Research/Libr/Mls/Mlslist.htm
  Forthcoming. Monumental inscriptions, recorded c.100 years ago

Lancashire

Cemeteries

- Lancashire Crematoria
  www.genuki.org.uk/big/eng/LAN/crematoria.shtml
  List with opening dates

- Liverpool & the Wirral Cemeteries
  freepages.genealogy.rootsweb.com/~lswlfhs/cemeteries.htm
  List

Institutional Collections

- Family History in Manchester
  www.manchester.gov.uk/libraries/arls/famhist.htm
  Includes notes on 'Cemetery records and monumental inscriptions' at
  Manchester Public Library

Brasses

- Monumental Brass Rubbings for England: Lancashire
  www.ashmol.co.uk/ash/departments/antiquities/brass/
  Click on 'Catalogue' and county. In the Ashmolean Museum, Oxford

- Lancashire
  www.mbs-brasses.co.uk/Lancashire.htm
  Bibliography of monumental brasses

Publications

- Lancashire Family History and Heraldry Society: Microfiche
  Publications: Monumental Inscriptions
  www.lancashire-fhhs.org.uk/mis-ag.htm
  Continued on 2 further pages

- Manchester & Lancashire Family History Society
  www.mlfhs.demon.co.uk/Bookshop/Index.html
  Click on title. List of the society's publications, including many parish
  registers and monumental inscriptions

- Ormskirk & District Family History Society Website
  www.odfhs.freeserve.co.uk/publications.html
  Publications page; includes some monumental inscriptions *etc.* on fiche.

Anfield
- Liverpool Cemeteries: [Anfield]
  freepages.genealogy.rootsweb.com/~liverpoolcem/Anfield1.htm
  Continued at **/Anfield2.htm**
  List of burials

Bickerstaffe
- Bickerstaffe Parish Churchyard, Bickerstaffe, Lancashire, England
  www.interment.net/data/eng/lancashire/bickerstaffe/bickerstaffe.htm

Bolton
- Bolton Saint Peter Parish Churchyard, Greater Manchester, England
  www.interment.net/data/eng/greatman/stpet__bolton/peter.htm

Briercliffe
- Saint James Churchyard, Briercliffe, Burnley, Lancashire, England
  www.interment.net/data/eng/lancashire/stjames/james.htm

Chadderton
- Chadderton Saint Mathew Churchyard, Greater Manchester, England
  www.interment.net/data/eng/greatman/saint__matt/mathew.htm

Colne
- Colne Cemetery, Colne, Lancashire, England
  www.interment.net/data/eng/lancashire/colne/colne.htm

Darwen
- Darwen Cemetery, Lancashire, England
  www.interment.net/data/eng/lancashire/darwen/darwen.htm

Edgworth
- Edgworth Congregational Churchyard, Edgworth, Bolton, Greater Manchester, England
  www.interment.net/data/eng/greatman/edgworth/edgworth.htm

Failsworth
- Failsworth Saint John Churchyard Greater Manchester, England
  www.interment.net/data/eng/greatman/stjohn/john.htm

Goodshaw
- Saint Mary and All Saints Churchyard, Goodshaw, Rossendale, Lancashire, England
  www.interment.net/data/eng/lancashire/stmary__good/stmary.htm

Hallfold
- Transcriptions from Grave Stones found in the Hallfold Congregational Church Cemetery, Lancashire
  www.xmission.com/%7Efamties/gen/inscript.htm

Halliwell
- Halliwell Saint Paul Churchyard, Greater Manchester, England
  www.interment.net/data/eng/greatman/stpaul__halliwell/stpaul.htm

Haslingden
- Haslingden Cemetery, Haslingden, Lancashire, England
  www.interment.net/data/eng/lancashire/haslingden/haslingden.htm

Heaton
- Heaton Cemetery, Greater Manchester, England
  www.interment.net/data/eng/greatman/heaton/heaton.htm

Holcombe
- Holcombe Emanuelle Parish Churchyard, Greater Manchester, England
  www.interment.net/data/eng/greatman/holcombe/emanuelle.htm

Lancaster
- Lancaster Priory Gravestones
  www.priory.lancs.ac.uk/tombs.html

Little Crosby
- List of people Buried at the Church by Surname in Alphabetical Order
  www.sunnyfields.freeserve.co.uk/church/
  surnames%20in%20alphabetical%20order.htm
  Monumental inscriptions at Little Crosby

Liverpool
- Liverpool Cemetery
  freepages.genealogy.rootsweb.com/~liverpoolcem
  In progress. General discussion

- St. James's Cemetery, Liverpool
  www.g0ifk/u-net.com
  Introduction, with database of inscriptions, *etc.*

Manchester

- Manchester Graveyards
  www.mlfhs.demon.co.uk/infobase/index.htm
  Click on title. List of graveyards

Padiham

- Padiham Church Cemetery, Padiham, Lancashire, England
  www.interment.net/data/eng/lancashire/padiham/padiham.htm

Rawtenstall

- Rawtenstall Cemetery, Rossendale, Lancashire, England
  www.interment.net/data/eng/lancashire/rawtenstall/rawten.htm

- Rawtenstall Saint Mary Churchyard, Lancashire, England
  www.interment.net/data/eng/lancashire/rawten__stmary/stmary.htm

- Sunnyside Baptist Chapel Yard, Rawtenstall, Lancashire, England
  www.interment.net/data/eng/lancashire/sunnyside/baptist.htm

- Unitarian Chapel Burial Ground, Rawtenstall, Lancashire, England
  www.interment.net/data/eng/lancashire/rawten__unitarian/unitarian.htm

Read

- Saint John Churchyard, Read, Lancashire, England
  www.interment.net/data/eng/lancashire/stjohn/stjohn.htm

Rochdale

- Rochdale Cemetery, Lancashire, England
  www.interment.net/data/eng/lancashire/rochdale/rochdale.htm

- Friends Quaker Burial Ground, Lancashire County, England
  www.interment.net/data/eng/lancashire/friends__quaker/quaker.htm
  In Rochdale

Rossendale

- Saint Ann Churchyard, Rossendale, Lancashire, England
  www.interment.net/data/eng/lancashire/stann__edge/stann.htm

St. Gabriel

- Saint Gabriel Churchyard, Lancashire County, England
  www.interment.net/data/eng/lancashire/gabriel/stgabe.htm
  Brief extracts, 20th c.

St. Helens

- St. Helens Graveyards
  www.genuki.org.uk/big/eng/LAN/StHelens/graveyards.html
  List

Salford

- Salford Burial Grounds
  www.salfordroots.com/page62.html

- Some Memorial Inscriptions: Salford, Lancashire: St. Thomas's Churchyard
  www.wishful-thinking.org.uk/Genuki/LAN/Salford/Mls.html

Thornton Cleveleys

- Christchurch Churchyard, Thornton Clevelys, Lancashire, England
  www.interment.net/data/eng/lancashire/christchurch/christchurch.htm

Tottington

- Tottington Saint Anne Churchyard, Bury, Greater Manchester, England
  www.interment.net/data/eng/greatman/stanne__tott/stanne.htm

Turton

- Turton Saint Anne Churchyard, Greater Manchester, England
  www.interment.net/data/eng/greatman/turton__anne/stanne.htm

Walton on the Hill

- Liverpool Cemeteries: [St. Mary's, Walton on the Hill]
  freepages.genealogy.rootsweb.com/~liverpoolcem/stmary.html
  Monumental inscriptions

Wheatley Carr

- Wheatley Carr Churchyard, Near Fence, Lancashire, England
  www.interment.net/data/eng/lancashire/wheatley/carr.htm

Leicestershire

Brasses
- Monumental Brass Rubbings for England: Leicestershire
  www.ashmol.co.uk/ash/departments/antiquities/brass/
  Click on 'Catalogue' and county. In the Ashmolean Museum, Oxford

- Leicestershire
  www.mbs-brasses.co.uk/Leicestershire.htm
  Bibliography of monumental brasses

Publications
- Sepulchral Effigies in Leicestershire and Rutland
  homepages.ntlworld.com/max.matthews/page07.htm
  Details of a CD to be published by Heart of Albion Press

- Max Wade-Matthews
  www.indigogroup.co.uk/albion/matthews.htm
  Details of the author's publications on Leicestershire inscriptions

Foston
- Graves in the Churchyard
  www.elektromail.freeserve.co.uk/stbart/gravesurname.html
  At Foston, Leicestershire

Leicester
- St. Martin's Cathedral Monuments
  uk.geocities.com/st__martins__leicester/monnames.htm
  Leicester

- The Cemeteries of the City of Leicester
  lrfhs.org.uk/cemeteries.html
  List with notes and photographs

- A Brief History of Welford Road Cemetery
  lrfhs.org.uk/welford.html
  In Leicester

- Welford Road Cemetery, Leicester
  uk.geocities.com/welford__road__cemetery/index.html
  Introduction; includes 'index of notable people buried in Welford Road Cemetery'.

Marshchapel
- Marshchapel
  freespace.virgin.net/fiona.poulton/marshchapel.htm
  Inscriptions from 51 headstones

Netherseal
- St. Peter Netherseal (Leicestershire) Monumental Inscriptions
  freepages.genealogy.rootsweb.com/~brett/seal/netherseal__mi.htm

Shepshed
- Memorials at Shepshed Cemetery
  gye.future.easyspace.com/shep.htm

Lincolnshire

Cemeteries
- Lincolnshire Cemeteries and Crematoria
  ukburials-cremations.co.uk/lincoln__cem__crem.htm
  List for North Lincolnshire

Web Page Collections
- Church Monuments and other Memorials of Interest
  www.churchmousewebsite.co.uk/monuments.htm
  Collection of monuments from various Lincolnshire churches

- Lincolnshire Village Memorials
  www.memorials-lincs.org.uk/index.html

Publications
- Lincolnshire Family History Society: Cemetery Registers
  www.genuki.org.uk/big/eng/LIN/lfhs/Publications/PubsCemeteryReg.htm
  Publications on fiche

- Lincolnshire Family History Society: Monumental Inscriptions
  www.genuki.org.uk/big/eng/LIN/lfhs/Publications/PubsMonumInscr.htm
  Fiche publications

Brasses
- Monumental Brass Rubbings for England: Lincolnshire
  www.ashmol.co.uk/ash/departments/antiquities/brass/
  Click on 'Catalogue' and county. In the Ashmolean Museum, Oxford

- Lincolnshire
  www.mbs-brasses.co.uk/Lincolnshire.htm
  Bibliography of monumental brasses

Bottesford
- Memorials in the Burial Grounds of St. Mary the Virgin, Bottesford
  freepages.genealogy.rootsweb.com/~framland/bb/bbindex.htm

Fulstow
- Fulstow
  freespace.virgin.net/fiona.poulton/Fulstow%20MI's.htm
  Inscriptions from 22 headstones

Old Clee
- Old Clee, near Grimsby, Lincolnshire
  www.churchmousewebsite.co.uk/old__clee.htm
  Notes on monuments

Utterby
- Utterby (St. Andrews)
  freespace.virgin.net/fiona.poulton/utterby.htm
  Inscriptions from 62 headstones

Wyham with Cadeby
- Wyham with Cadeby
  freespace.virgin.net/fiona.poulton/wyham.htm
  5 inscriptions

London & Middlesex

Cemeteries
See also Essex
- Victorian London Cemeteries
  www.gendocs.demon.co.uk/cem.html
  List with some brief notes

- City of London Cemetery
  **www.cityoflondon.gov.uk/leisure__heritage/
  libraries__archives__museums__galleries/clro/pdf/cemetary.PDF**
  Includes details of records

Indexes
- Monumental Inscriptions
  www.west-middlesex-fhs.org.uk/fwm-indx.html
  Click on title. West Middlesex Family History Society service

Publications
- West Middlesex Family History Society: Publications
  www.west-middlesex-fhs.org/fwm-pub.html
  Includes monumental inscriptions on fiche

- [London and North Middlesex Family History Society]: Indexes
  www.lnmfhs.dircon.co.uk/serchidx.htm
  Publications, including monumental inscriptions on fiche

- Hillingdon Family History Society: society publications
  users.rootsweb.com/~enghfhs/publish.html
  Includes a few monumental inscriptions on fiche

Brasses
- Monumental Brass Rubbings for England: Middlesex
  www.ashmol.co.uk/ash/departments/antiquities/brass/
  Click on 'Catalogue' and county. In the Ashmolean Museum, Oxford

- Middlesex (including London)
  www.mbs-brasses.co.uk/Middlesex.htm
  Bibliography of monumental brasses

Abney Park
- Abney Park Cemetery Index
  www.bigenealogy.com/articles/abneypark.htm
  Aims to provide on-line index to 194,815 burials. In progress

- Abney Park Cemetery Trust
  www.abney-park.org.uk/
  Introduction only

- Abney Park Cemetery Indexing Project
  www.cam.org/~hopkde/project.html

Highgate
- Friends of Highgate Cemetery
  www.highgate-cemetery.org/index.asp
  Introduction only

Kensal Green
- Kensal Green Cemetery, London
  www.xs4all.nl/~androom/dead/kensal.htm
  Introduction only

Tottenham
- All Hallows Monumental Inscriptions
  **www.mickbruff.pwp.blueyonder.co.uk/highroad/allhallows/mis/
  misindex.html**

  Tottenham

Norfolk

Institutional Collections
- Norfolk Family History Society: Monumental Inscriptions Project: Records at Kirby Hall
  www.norfolkfhs.org.uk/church/mon__ins.html
  Extensive list of the Society's transcriptions available for look-up

Web Page Collections
- Norfolk Gravestone Photograph Resource
  www.gravestonephotos.com/norfolk/index.htm

- The Norfolk Heraldry Society
  www.norfolkheraldry.co.uk/
  Includes discussions of heraldic monuments in churches

Brasses
- Monumental Brass Rubbings for England: Norfolk
  www.ashmol.co.uk/ash/departments/antiquities/brass/
  Click on 'Catalogue' and county. In the Ashmolean Museum, Oxford

- Norfolk
  www.mbs-brasses.co.uk/Norfolk.htm
  Bibliography of monumental brasses

Burnham & Walsingham Deanery
- The Norfolk Heraldry Society: Burnham & Walsingham Deanery
  www.norfolkheraldry.co.uk/Deaneries/Burnham/Burnham.htm
  Includes brief notes on heraldry in each church

Diss
- Diss Cemetery and Chapel
  www.diss.gov.uk/cemetery.htm
  Brief description

East Barsham
- The Norfolk Heraldry Society: East Barsham
  www.norfolkheraldry.co.uk/Deaneries/Burnham/east__barsham.htm
  Monumental inscriptions and heraldry

East Harling
- The Norfolk Heraldry Society: East Harling Church
  www.norfolkheraldry.co.uk/Deaneries/Thetford/East%20Harling/
  east__harling.htm
  Discussion of heraldic inscriptions

Gorlestone
- Gorleston Cemetery, Gorleston, Norfolk County, England
  www.interment.net/data/eng/norfolk/gorleston/gorleston.htm

- Gorleston Saint Andrew Churchyard, Gorleston, Norfolk County, England
  www.interment.net/data/eng/norfolk/standrew/gorleston.htm

Norwich
- Gravestone Photographs: St Clements Parish Church, Norwich, Norfolk
  www.gravestonephotos.com/norfolk/norwich/stclement.htm

- Gravestone Photographs: St George Colegate Parish Church, Norwich, Norfolk
  www.gravestonephotos.com/norfolk/norwich/stgeorgecolegate.htm

- Gravestone Photographs: St Gregory Parish Church, Norwich, Norfolk
  www.gravestonephotos.com/norfolk/norwich/stgregory.htm

- Gravestone Photographs: St Laurence Parish Church, Norwich, Norfolk
  www.gravestonephotos.com/norfolk/norwich/stlaurence.htm

- Gravestone Photographs: St Michael Coslany Parish Church, Norwich, Norfolk
  www.gravestonephotos.com/norfolk/norwich/stmichaelcoslany.htm

- Gravestone Photographs: St Peter Mancroft Parish Church, Norwich, Norfolk
  www.myroots.couk/gravestones/norfolk/norwich/stpetermancroft.htm

- Gravestone Photographs: St Savour Parish Church, Norwich, Norfolk
  www.gravestonephotos.com/norfolk/norwich/stsavour.htm

Trunch
- Monumental Inscriptions for Trunch
  www.trunchnorfolk.cwc.net/monumental.htm

Northamptonshire

Brasses
- Monumental Brass Rubbings for England: Northamptonshire
  www.ashmol.co.uk/ash/departments/antiquities/brass/
  Click on 'Catalogue' and county. In the Ashmolean Museum, Oxford

- Northamptonshire
  www.mbs-brasses.co.uk/Northamptonshire.htm
  Bibliography of monumental brasses

Northumberland

Institutional Collections
  See also Durham
- Northumberland Archive Service: Transcripts in Berwick upon Tweed
  Record Office
  www.swinhope.demon.co.uk/NRO/Berwick.html
  Of parish registers, monumental inscriptions, *etc.*

- Newcastle upon Tyne City Libraries & Arts. Local Studies Library.
  Genealogy Guide no.6. Monumental Inscriptions
  www.swinhope.demon.co.uk/genuki/NBL/NCLLib/NCLGG6.html

- Northumberland Monumental Inscriptions
  www.ndfhs.org.uk/Library/index.html
  Click on title. In the library of the Northumberland & Durham Family
  History Society

Publications
- Northumberland & Durham Family History Society Publications on
  Microfiche
  www.ndfhs.org.uk/Fiche.html
  Includes parish registers, monumental inscriptions, *etc.*

Brasses
- Monumental Brass Rubbings for England: Northumberland
  www.ashmol.co.uk/ash/departments/antiquities/brass/
  Click on 'Catalogue' and county. In the Ashmolean Museum, Oxford

- Northumberland
  www.mbs-brasses.co.uk/Northumberland.htm
  Bibliography of monumental brasses

Allenheads
- Allenheads Methodist Chapel, Northumberland
  freepages.genealogy.rootsweb.com/~rprobert/photos/nbl/allenheads/
  chapel/04.htm
  Inscriptions

Ashburton
- Ashburton Roman Catholic Cemetery Monumental Inscriptions
  www.cs.ncl.ac.uk/genuki/Transcriptions/NBL/Ashburton.html
  In Newcastle

Church Bank
- Church Bank Cemetery, Northumberland, England
  www.interment.net/data/eng/northumberland/churchbank/
  churchbank.htm

Heddon on the Wall
- The Monumental Inscriptions of the Church and Churchyard of St. Andrew's, Heddon-on-the-Wall, Northumberland
  www.heddon.currantbun.com/archive/inscript/index.htm

Newburn
- Newburn Saint Michael & All Angels Churchyard, Newburn, Northumberland, England
  www.interment.net/data/eng/northumberland/stmike/angels.htm

Whorlton
- St John's Church, Whorlton: Monumental Inscriptions
  www.cs.ncl.ac.uk/genuki/Transcriptions/NBL/Whorlton.html

Nottinghamshire

Look-ups
- List of Monumental Inscriptions available for searches through the Notts. Look-up Exchange
  freespace.virgin.net/n.faulkes/lookup/inscript.htm

Publications
- Nottinghamshire Family History Society: the Online Shop
  www.nottsfhs.org.uk/bookshop/system/index.html
  Includes monumental inscriptions published by the society

Brasses
- Monumental Brass Rubbings for England: Nottinghamshire
  www.ashmol.co.uk/ash/departments/antiquities/brass/
  Click on 'Catalogue' and county. In the Ashmolean Museum, Oxford

- Nottinghamshire
  www.mbs-brasses.co.uk/Nottinghamshire.htm
  Bibliography of monumental brasses

Allenheads
- Allenheads Methodist Chapel, Northumberland
  freepages.genealogy.rootsweb.com/~rprobert/photos/nbl/allenheads/
  chapel/04.htm

  Inscriptions

Burton Joyce
- Burton Joyce: St. Helen Monuments
  southwellchurches.nottingham.ac.uk/b01/hmonumnt.html

Carrington
- Carrington: St. John Monuments
  southwellchurches.nottingham.ac.uk/c02/hmonumnt.html

Cossall
- Cossall Village: Memorial Inscriptions
  homepages.ntlworld.com/david.scarle/cossall.htm#Memorial

Cotgrave
- Cotgrave: All Saints Monuments
southwellchurches.nottingham.ac.uk/c01/hmonumnt.html

Daybrook
- Daybrook: St. Paul's Monuments
southwellchurches.nottingham.ac.uk/d01/hmonumnt.html

Mansfield
- List of Gravestones in Mansfield Churchyard at 1800
www.oldnotts.co.uk/graves1801.htm

- List of Graves Cleared from St. Peter's Churchyard, Mansfield, Ntts
freespace.virgin.net/n.faulkes/genuki/NTT/mansfield/graves.htm
Cleared in 1905

- List of Graves cleared from St. Peter's Churchyard, Mansfield, Notts
www.oldnotts.co.uk/data/graves.htm

New Basford
- New Basford: St. Augustine Monuments
southwellchurches.nottingham.ac.uk/b03/hmonumnt.html

Newark
- Newark: St. Mary Magdalene Monuments
southwellchurches.nottingham.ac.uk/n02/hmonumnt.html

Nottingham
- Nottingham: St. Peter Monuments
southwellchurches.nottingham.ac.uk/n01/hmonumnt.html

- Nottingham Cemeteries
www2.prestel/renfrew/history/NTT/Nottingham/cemeteries.html
Brief discussion

- Nottingham Cemeteries and Burial Grounds
www.geocities.com/whittakergen/notts/cems/index.htm
Introduction only

- Monumental Inscriptions in the Baptist Burial Ground, Mount Street, Nottingham
www2.prestel.co.uk/renfrew/history/NTT/Nottingham/mountst.html

Sutton in Ashfield
- Churchyard Walk
www.oldnotts.co.uk/sutton/churchyard/churchyard.htm
A small selection of Sutton in Ashfield inscriptions

- Sutton-in-Ashfield Cemetery
www.oldnotts.co.uk/sutton/cemetery/index.htm

Oxfordshire

Web Page Collections
- Monumental Inscriptions: Oxfordshire
  www.towball.freewire.co.uk/Oxfordshire.htm
  Index. Entries from Cholsey, Goring and South Moreton at present, but more may be added

- Inscriptions from Oxfordshire churches
  www.towball.freewire.co.uk/inscr__3.htm
  Selected inscriptions from various parishes

Brasses
- Monumental Brass Rubbings for England: Oxfordshire
  www.ashmol.co.uk/ash/departments/antiquities/brass/
  Click on 'Catalogue' and county. In the Ashmolean Museum, Oxford

- Oxfordshire
  www.mbs-brasses.co.uk/Oxfordshire.htm
  Bibliography of monumental brasses

Chilton
- Memorial Inscriptions, All Saints, Chilton, Oxon
  users.ox.ac.uk/~malcolm/genuki/big/eng/OXF/Chilton/Mns051.HTM
  Continued at **/Mns100.HTM**
  Index also available at **/MlndAC.HTM** and on 3 further pages

Cholsey
- Inscriptions from Parish Church of St. Mary, Colsey, Oxfordshire
  www.towball.freewire.co.uk/inscri15.htm
  Selected inscriptions

Cuddesdon
- Transcribed Names from Memorials and Graves in Cuddesdon Churchyard, Oxfordshire, UK
  users.ox.ac.uk/~malcolm/genuki/big/eng/OXF/Cuddesdon/mi.txt

Oxford
- Balliol College Memorial Inscriptions
  users.ox.ac.uk/~ballinfo/history/memorial.htm

Watchfield
- Watchfield Cemetery, Watchfield, Oxfordshire, England
  www.interment.net/data/eng/oxfordshire/watchfield/watch.htm

Rutland

Brasses
- Monumental Brass Rubbings for England: Rutland
  www.ashmol.co.uk/ash/departments/antiquities/brass/
  Click on 'Catalogue' and county. In the Ashmolean Museum, Oxford

- Rutland
  www.mbs-brasses.co.uk/Rutland.htm
  Bibliography of monumental brasses

Shropshire

Institutional Collections
- Transcripts of Monumental Inscriptions
  www.genuki.org.uk/big/eng/SAL/SFHS/MI__Transcripts.html
  Comprehensive list of transcripts in various repositories, with locations

Indexes
- MI Surname Index: Monumental Inscriptions of Shropshire
  www.genuki.org.uk/big/eng/SAL/SFHS/MI__SurnameIndex.html
  Index to transcripts held by the Society

- List of Transcripts included in Computerized Index of MI's
  www.genuki.org.uk/big/eng/SAL/SFHS/MI__List.html

Brasses
- Monumental Brass Rubbings for England: Shropshire
  www.ashmol.co.uk/ash/departments/antiquities/brass/
  Click on 'Catalogue' and county. In the Ashmolean Museum, Oxford

- Shropshire
  www.mbs-brasses.co.uk/Shropshire.htm
  Bibliography of monumental brasses

Publications
- Shropshire Family History Society: Monumental Inscriptions on Microfiche
  www.genuki.org.uk/big/eng/SAL/SFHS/MI__Fiche.html

- Shropshire Family History Society: Monumental Inscriptions available as Photocopies
  www.genuki.org.uk/big/eng/SAL/SFHS/MI__Photocopies.htm

Alveley
- St. Mary the Virgin, Alveley, Shropshire, Monumental Inscriptions
  uk-transcriptions.accessgenealogy.com/Alveley%20MI's.htm

Quatt
- Monumental Inscriptions from St. Andrews, Quatt
  uk-transcriptions.accessgenealogy.com/Quatt%20MI's.htm

Somerset

Indexes
- Somerset Monumental Inscriptions
  www.sdfhs.org/Sommis.htm
  Index in progress

Web Page Collections
- Wishful Thinking's GENUKI: Somerset Pages: Memorial Inscription Collection
  www.wishful-thinking.org.uk/genuki/SOM/Mls.html

Brasses
- Monumental Brass Rubbings for England: Somerset
  www.ashmole.co.uk/ash/departments/antiquities/brass/
  Click on 'Catalogue' and county. In the Ashmolean Museum, Oxford

- Somerset
  www.mbs-brasses.co.uk/Somerset.htm
  Bibliography of monumental brasses

East Coker
- Some Memorial Inscriptions, East Coker, Somerset. St. Michael's Churchyard
  www.wishful-thinking.org.uk/genuki/SOM/EastCoker/Mls.html

Frome
- Frome East Woodlands Memorial Inscriptions
  www.gomezsmarts.free-online.co.uk/prs/ewoodsmi.htm

- Some Memorial Inscriptions: Frome, Somerset: Christchurch, and Dissenters Cemetery, Vallis Way
  www.wishful-thinking.org.uk/SOM/Frome/Mls.html

Nunney
- Extracts from Nunney Parish Registers: Memorial Inscriptions
  www.gomezsmarts.free-online.co.uk/nunneypr.htm#Mls

Over Stowey
- The Parish Church of St. Peter & St. Paul, Over Stowey, Somerset
  freespace.virgin.net/tim.whittingham/Over_Stowey_Grave_Inscript.htm
  Monumental Inscriptions

Taunton
- Monumental Inscriptions in St. Mary Magdalene's Church, Taunton
  www.parkhouse.org.uk/transcr/tsm_mi.html
  From Joshua Toolmin's *The history of Taunton ...*, originally published 1822

Wells
- Friends of Mendip Hospital Cemtery
  www.Lyatt.freeserve.co.uk/
  At Wells; introduction only

Staffordshire

Web Page Collections
- Wishful Thinking's GENUKI: Staffordshire Pages
  www.wishful-thinking.org.uk/genuki/STS/Mls.html

Look-ups
- Staffordshire Look-up Exchange
  freespace.virgin.net/m.harbach/sts.html
  Look-ups of many parish registers and monumental inscriptions *etc.*
  offered

Publications
- B.M.S.G.H. Bookshop, Staffordshire: Parishes, Districts & other places
  www.bmsgh.org/bookshop/staffs/st__a.htm
  Parish registers and monumental inscriptions available in fiche & book
  formats

Brasses
- Monumental Brass Rubbings for England: Staffordshire
  www.ashmol.co.uk/ash/departments/antiquities/brass/
  Click on 'Catalogue' and county. In the Ashmolean Museum, Oxford

- Staffordshire
  www.mbs-brasses.co.uk/staffordshire.htm
  Bibliography of monumental brasses

Abbots Bromley
- Some Memorial Inscriptions: Abbots Bromley, Staffordshire: St.
  Nicholas's Churchyard
  www.wishful-thinking.org.uk/genuki/STS/AbbotsBromley/Mls.html

Alstonfield
- Some Memorial Inscriptions: Alstonfield, Staffordshire: St. Peter's
  Churchyard
  www.wishful-thinking.org.uk/genuki/STS/Alstonfield/Mls.html

Alton
- Some Memorial Inscriptions: Alton, Staffordshire: St. Peter's Churchyard
  and St. John the Baptist R. C. church
  www.wishful-thinking.org.uk/genuki/STS/Alton/Mls.htm

Betley
- Introduction to the Betley Monumental Inscription Book
  bfhs.co.uk/betley__memorials__book.htm

Bilston
- Bilston St. Mary: Memorials inside the Church
  www.genuki.org.uk/big/eng/STS/Bilston/StMary/Memorials.html

Blore
- Some Memorial Inscriptions: Blore-Ray, Staffordshire: St. Bartholomew's
  Churchyard
  www.wishful-thinking.org.uk/genuki/STS/BloreRay/Mls.html

Bradley
- Headstone Inscriptions taken from Bradley Churchyard in the County of
  Stafford, England
  www.geocities.com/ann__margetson/bradley.htm
  www.geocities.com/Athens/Academy/2214/bradley.htm

Bradley in the Moors
- Some Memorial Inscriptions: Bradley in the Moors, Staffordshire: St.
  Leonard's Churchyard
  www.wishful-thinking.org.uk/genuki/STS/BradleyintheMoors/Mls.html

Burslem
- Some Memorial Inscriptions: Burslem, Staffordshire: St. George's
  Churchyard
  www.wishful-thinking.org.uk/genuki/STS/Burslem/Mls.html

Butterton
- Some Memorial Inscriptions: Butterton, Staffordshire: St. Bartholomew's
  Churchyard
  www.wishful-thiking.org.uk/genuki/STS/Butterton/Mls.html

Cauldon
- Some Memorial Inscriptions: Cauldon, Staffordshire: St. Mary & St.
  Lawrence's Churchyard and Cemetery
  www.wishful-thinking.org.uk/genuki/STS/Cauldon/Mls.html

Caverswall

- Some Memorial Inscriptions: Caverswall with Weston Coyney, Staffordshire: St. Peter with St. Andrew's Churchyard, and Cemetery
www.wishful-thinking.org.uk/genuki/STS/Caverswall/Mls.html

Cheadle

- Some Memorial Inscriptions: Cheadle, Staffordshire: St. Giles the Abbot's Churchyard
www.wishful-thinking.org.uk/genuki/STS/Cheadle/Mls.html

Checkley

- Some Memorial Inscriptions: Checkley, Staffordshire: St. Mary & All Saints' Churchyard
www.wishful-thinking.org.uk/genuki/STS/Checkley/Mls.html

Cheddleton

- Some Memorial Inscriptions: Cheddleton, Staffordshire: St. Edward's Churchyard
www.wishful-thinking.org.uk/genuki/STS/Cheddleton/Mls.html

Cotton

- Some Memorial Inscriptions: Cotton, Staffordshire, C. of E. Cemetery, Cotton Lane
www.wishful-thinking.org.uk/genuki/STS/Cotton/Mls.html

Croxden

- Some Memorial Inscriptions: Croxden, Staffordshire: St. Giles Churchyard
www.wishful-thinking.org.uk/genuki/STS/Croxden/Mls.html

Denstone

- Some Memorial Inscriptions: Denstone, Staffordshire: All Saints' Churchyard
www.wishful-thinking.org.uk/genuki/STS/Denstone/Mls.html

Dilhorne

- Some Memorial Inscriptions: Dilhorne, Staffordshire: All Saints Churchyard
www.wishful-thinking.org.uk/genuki/STS/Dilhorne/Mls.html

Draycott in the Moors

- Some Memorial Inscriptions: Draycott in the Moors, Staffordshire: St. Margaret's Churchyard
www.wishful-thinking.org.uk/genuki/STS/DraycottintheMoors/Mls.html

Ellastone

- Some Memorial Inscriptions: Ellastone, Staffordshire: St. Peter's Churchyard
www.wishful-thinking.org.uk/genuki/STS/Ellastone/Mls.html

Foxt

- Some Memorial Inscriptions: Foxt, Staffordshire: St. Mark's Churchyard
www.wishful-thinking.org.uk/genuki/STS/Foxt/Mls.html

Freehay

- Some Memorial Inscriptions: Freehay, Staffordshire: St. Chad's Churchyard
www.wishful-thinking.org.uk/genuki/STS/Freehay/Mls.html

Gnosall

- Headstone Inscriptions from Gnosall Churchyard, Stafford
geocities.com/bjmargetson/Gnosall.htm

Grindon

- Some Memorial Inscriptions: Grindon, Staffordshire: All Saints Churchyard
www.wishful-thinking.org.uk/genuki/STS/Grindon/Mls.html

Haughton

- Headstone Inscriptions taken from Haughton Parish Church in the County of Stafford, England
www.geocities.com/ann__margetson/haughton.htm
www.geocities.com/Athens/Academy/2214/haughton.htm

Ilam

- Some Memorial Inscriptions: Ilam, Staffordshire: The Holy Cross Churchyard
www.wishful-thinking.org.uk/genuki/STS/Ilam/Mls.html

Kingsley

- Some Memorial Inscriptions: Kingsley, Staffordshire: St. Werburg's Churchyard
www.wishful-thinking.org.uk/genuki/STS/Kingsley/Mls.html

Leek
- Some Memorial Inscriptions: Leek, Staffordshire: Leek Cemetery
  www.wishful-thinking.org.uk/genuki/STS/Leek/Mls.html

Newborough
- Some Memorial Inscriptions: Newborough, Staffordshire: All Saints Churchyard
  www.wishful-thinking.org.uk/genuki/STS/Newborough/Mls.html

Newcastle under Lyme
- Newcastle Cemetery Action Group
  ww2.fenetre.co.uk/~ncag
  Introduction, with list of threatened graves

Norbury
- Headstone Inscriptions taken from Norbury Churchyard, Stafford
  geocities.com/bjmargetson/Norbury.htm

Oakamoor
- Some Memorial Inscriptions: Oakamoor, Staffordshire: Memorial Free Church
  www.wishful-thinking.org.uk/genuki/STS/Oakamoor/Mls.html

Onecote
- Some Memorial Inscriptions: Onecote, Staffordshire: St. Luke's Churchyard
  www.wishful-thinking.org.uk/genuki/STS/Onecote/Mls.html

Penkhull
- Penkhull, St. Thomas Church, Stoke on Trent
  geocities.com/bjmargetson/penkhull.htm
  Index to inscriptions

Rocester
- Some Memorial Inscriptions: Rocester, Staffordshire: St. Michael's Churchyard and Cemetery
  www.wishful-thinking.org.uk/genuki/STS/Rocester/Mls.html

Stanton
- Some Memorial Inscriptions: Stanton, Staffordshire: St. Mary's Churchyard
  www.wishful-thinking.org.uk/genuki/STS/Stanton/Mls.html

Swynnerton
- [St. Mary's, Swynnerton: Graves Records]
  www.btinternet.com/~stmarys/records/database/graves/graves.htm

Walsall
- St. Mary's, The Mount, Walsall: Monumental Inscriptions
  www.platt-grigg.accessgenealogy.com/about.html

- St. Mary's, The Mount, Walsall, Staffordshire
  uk-transcriptions.accessgenealogy.com/St.Mary's%20RC20MI's.txt

Waterfall
- Some Memorial Inscriptions: Waterfall, Staffordshire: St. James & St. Bartholomew's Churchyard
  www.wishful-thinking.org.uk/genuki/STS/Waterfall/Mls.html

Weston Coyney
See Caverswall

Wetton
- Some Memorial Inscriptions: Wetton, Staffordshire: St. Margaret's Churchyard
  www.wishful-thinking.org.uk/genuki/STS/Wetton/Mls.html

Whiston
- Some Memorial Inscriptions: Whiston, Staffordshire: St. Mildred's Churchyard
  www.wishful-thinking.org.uk/genuki/STS/Whiston/Mls.html

Suffolk

Web Page Collections
- Suffolk Gravestone Photograph Resource
  www.gravestonephotos.com/suffolk/index.htm
  Collection of web-pages, separately listed below

Brasses
- Monumental Brass Rubbings for England: Suffolk
  www.ashmol.co.uk/ash/departments/antiquities/brass/
  Click on 'Catalogue' and county. In the Ashmolean Museum, Oxford

- Suffolk
  www.mbs-brasses.co.uk/Suffolk.htm
  Bibliography of monumental brasses

Barnby
- Gravestone Photographs: St John the Baptist Parish Church, Barnby, Suffolk
  www.gravestonephotos.com/suffolk/barnby.htm

Barsham with Shipmeadow
- Gravestone Photographs: The Holy Trinity Parish Church, Barsham with Shipmeadow, Suffolk
  www.gravestonephotos.com/suffolk/barsham.htm

Benhall
- Gravestone Photographs: St Mary's Parish Church, Benhall, Suffolk
  www.gravestonephotos.com/suffolk/benhall.htm

Brockdish
- Gravestone Photographs: St Peter & St Paul's Parish Church, Brockdish, Suffolk
  www.gravestonephotos.com/suffolk/brockdish.htm

Burstall
- Gravestone Photographs: St Mary's Parish Church, Burstall, Suffolk
  www.gravestonephotos.com/suffolk/burstall.htm

Corton
- Corton Saint Bartholomew Churchyard, Corton, Suffolk, England
  www.interment.net/data/eng/suffolk/corton/corton.htm

- Gravestone Photographs: St Bartholomew's Parish Church, Corton, Suffolk
  www.gravestonephotos.com/suffolk/corton.htm

Covehithe
- Gravestone Photographs: St Andrew's Parish Church, Covehithe, Suffolk
  www.gravestonephotos.com/suffolk/covehithe.htm

Elmset
- Gravestone Photographs: St Peter's Parish Church, Elmset, Suffolk
  www.gravestonephotos.com/suffolk/elmset.htm

Elveden
- Gravestone Photographs: St Andrew and St Patrick Parish Church, Elveden, Suffolk
  www.gravestonephotos.com/suffolk/elvedon.htm

Eyke
- Gravestone Photographs: Parish Church, Eyke, Suffolk
  www.gravestonephotos.com/suffolk/eyke.htm

Fressingfield
- Gravestone Photographs: Parish Church, Fressingfield, Suffolk
  www.gravestonephotos.com/suffolk/fressingfield.htm

Frostenden
- Gravestone Photographs: Parish Church, Frostenden, Suffolk
  www.gravestonephotos.com/suffolk/frostenden.htm

Gunton
- Gravestone Photographs: St Peter's Parish Church, Gunton, Suffolk
  www.gravestonephotos.com/suffolk/gunton.htm

Henstead cum Hulver
- Gravestone Photographs: St Mary's Parish Church, Henstead cum Hulver, Suffolk
  www.gravestonephotos.com/suffolk/henstead.htm

Herringfleet
- Gravestone Photographs: St Margarets Parish Church, Herringfleet, Suffolk
  www.gravestonephotos.com/suffolk/herringfleet.htm

Hingham
- Gravestone Photographs: St Mary's Parish Church, Hingham, Suffolk
  www.gravestonephotos.com/suffolk/hingham.htm

Hintlesham
- Gravestone Photographs: St Nicholas Parish Church, Hintlesham, Suffolk
  www.gravestonephotos.com/suffolk/hintlesham.htm

Ipswich
- Gravestone Photographs: St Lawrence Church, Ipswich, Suffolk
  www.gravestonephotos.com/suffolk/ipswich/stlawrence.htm

- Gravestone Photographs: St Mary-le-Tower Church, Ipswich, Suffolk
  www.gravestonephotos.com/suffolk/ipswichstmary.htm

Kersey
- Gravestone Photographs: St Mary's Parish Church, Kersey, Suffolk
  www.gravestonephotos.com/suffolk/kersey.htm

Kirkley
- Gravestone Photographs: Municipal Cemetery, Kirkley, Suffolk
  www.gravestonephotos.com/suffolk/kirkleymc.htm

- Kirkley Cemtery, Suffolk, England
  www.interment.net/data/eng/suffolk/kirkley/kirkley.htm

- Gravestone Photographs: St Peter & St John Parish Church, Kirkley, Suffolk
  www.gravestonephotos.com/suffolk/kirkley.htm

Lowestoft
- Gravestone Photographs: Municipal Cemetery, Lowestoft, Suffolk
  www.gravestonephotos.com/suffolk/lowestoftmc.htm

- Lowestoft Municipal Cemetery, Lowestoft, Suffolk, England
  www.interment.net/data/eng/suffolk/lowestoft/lowestroft.htm

- Lowestoft Saint Margaret Churchyard, Lowestoft, Suffolk, England
  www.interment.net/data/eng/suffolk/margaret/stmarg.htm
  428 entries, giving dates of death, and ages

- Gravestone Photographs: St Margaret's Parish Church, Lowestoft, Suffolk
  www.gravestonephotos.com/suffolk/lowestoft.htm

Mettingham
- Gravestone Photographs: All Saints Parish Church, Mettingham, Suffolk
  www.gravestonephotos.com/suffolk/mettingham.htm

Mutford
- Gravestone Photographs: St Andrew's Parish Church, Mutford, Suffolk
  www.gravestonephotos.com/suffolk/mutford.htm

Naughton
- Gravestone Photographs: St Mary's Parish Church, Naughton, Suffolk
  www.gravestonephotos.com/suffolk/naughton.htm

Nedging
- Gravestone Photographs: Parish Church, Nedging, Suffolk
  www.gravestonephotos.com/suffolk/nedging.htm

North Cove
- Gravestone Photographs: St Botolph's Parish Church, North Cove, Suffolk
  www.gravestonephotos.com/suffolk/northcove.htm

Oulton
- Gravestone Photographs: St Michael Church, Oulton, Suffolk
  www.gravestonephotos.com/suffolk/oulton.htm

Pakefield
- Gravestone Photographs: All Saints & St. Margaret's Parish Church, Pakefield, Suffolk
  www.gravestonephotos.com/suffolk/pakefield.htm

Rickinghall
- Gravestone Photographs: Parish Church, Rickinghall, Suffolk
  www.gravestonephotos.com/suffolk/rickinghall.htm

Rushmere
- Gravestone Photographs: Parish Church, Rushmere, Suffolk
www.gravestonephotos.com/suffolk/rushmere.htm

Shipmeadow
- Gravestone Photographs: Parish Church, Shipmeadow, Suffolk
www.gravestonephotos.com/suffolk/shipmeadow.htm

Somerleyton
- Gravestone Photographs: St Mary Parish Church, Somerleyton, Suffolk
www.gravestonephotos.com/suffolk/somerleyton.htm

South Cove
- Gravestone Photographs: St Laurence Parish Church, South Cove, Suffolk
www.gravestonephotos.com/suffolk/southcove.htm

Southwold
- Gravestone Photographs: St Edmunds Parish Church, Southwold, Suffolk
www.gravestonephotos.com/suffolk/southwold.htm

Stanton
- Gravestone Photographs: Parish Church, Stanton, Suffolk
www.gravestonephotos.com/suffolk/stanton.htm

Sternfield
- Gravestone Photographs: St Mary Magdalene Parish Church, Sternfield, Suffolk
www.gravestonephotos.com/suffolk/sternfield.htm

Stradbroke
- Gravestone Photographs: Parish Church, Stradbroke, Suffolk
www.gravestonephotos.com/suffolk/stradbroke.htm
Photographs forthcoming

Stratford St. Mary
- Gravestone Photographs: St Mary's Parish Church, Stratford St Mary, Suffolk
www.gravestonephotos.com/suffolk/stratfordstmary.htm

Thorpe Abbotts
- Gravestone Photographs: All Saints Parish Church, Thorpe Abbotts, Suffolk
www.gravestonephotos.com/suffolk/thorpeabbotts.htm

Tunstall
- Gravestone Photographs: St Michael and All Angels Parish Church, Tunstall, Suffolk
www.gravestonephotos.com/suffolk/tunstall.htm

Wattisfield
- Gravestone Photographs: St Margaret's Parish Church, Wattisfield, Suffolk
www.gravestonephotos.com/suffolk/wattisfield.htm

Weston
- Gravestone Photographs: St Peter's Parish Church, Weston, Suffolk
www.gravestonephotos.com/suffolk/weston.htm

Whatfield
- Gravestone Photographs: St Margaret's Parish Church, Whatfield, Suffolk
www.gravestonephotos.com/suffolk/whatfield.htm

Wherstead
- St. Mary's Church and Churchyard Wherstead, Suffolk: monumental inscriptions
www.merrill.org/wherstead/church/St_Marys_Church_MI.pdf

Wingfield
- Gravestone Photographs: Parish Church, Wingfield, Suffolk
www.gravestonephotos.com/suffolk/wingfield.htm

Wrentham
- Gravestone Photographs: St Nicholas Parish Church, Wrentham, Suffolk
www.gravestonephotos.com/suffolk/wrentham.htm

Surrey

Web Page Collections
- Monumental Inscriptions: Surrey
  www.towball.freewire.co.uk/surrey.htm
  From Bletchingley, Chobham, Esher, and Shere. More may be added

Publications
- East Surrey Family History Society Bookstall
  www.eastsurreyfhs.org.uk/publics.htm
  Includes monumental inscriptions *etc.*

Brasses
- Monumental Brass Rubbings for England: Surrey
  www.ashmol.co.uk/ash/departments/antiquities/brass/
  Click on 'Catalogue' and county. In the Ashmolean Museum, Oxford

- Surrey
  www.mbs-brasses.co.uk/Surrey.htm
  Bibliography of monumental brasses

Bletchingley
- Inscriptions from St. Mary the Virgin, Bletchingley, Surrey
  www.towball.freewire.co.uk/inscr10.htm

Brookwood
- Brookwood Cemetery
  www.brookwoodcemetery.info/
  Introduction only

- The Brookwood Cemetery Society
  www.surreyweb.org.uk/bcs/index.htm
  Introduction, with note on the society's project to record inscriptions

- Brookwood Cemetery (aka London Necropolis or Woking Cemetery), Woking, Surrey, England
  www.interment.net/data/eng/surrey/brookwood/woking.htm

Chobham
- Inscriptions from St. Lawrence, Chobham
  www.towball.freewire.co.uk/inscr__6.htm
  Selected inscriptions

Esher
- Inscriptions from Christchurch, Esher, Surrey
  www.towball.freewire.co.uk/inscri17.htm
  Selected inscriptions

Nunhead
- Friends of Nunhead Cemetery
  www.fonc.org.uk
  Introduction only

Shere
- Inscriptions from St. James, Shere
  www.towball.freewire.co.uk/inscr__5.htm
  Selected inscriptions

West Norwood
- Friends of West Norwood Cemetery
  www.anoraque.demon.co.uk/fownc/index.htm
  Introduction only

Sussex

Indexes
- Monumental Inscriptions: Sussex
  www.towball.freewire.co.uk/Sussex.htm
  Index. From Bosham, Church Norton and Midhurst at present, but more may be added

- The Tombstones & Burials Index
  www.sfhg.org.uk/tombstones.html
  A Sussex Family History Group offline index; includes lists of churchyards and surnames

Brasses
- Monumental Brass Rubbings for England: Sussex
  www.ashmol.co.uk/ash/departments/antiquities/brass/
  Click on 'Catalogue' and county. In the Ashmolean Museum, Oxford

- Sussex
  www.mbs-brasses.co.uk/Sussex.htm
  Bibliography of monumental brasses

Publications
- Hastings and Rother Family History Society: H.R.F.H.S. Bookshop
  www.hrfhs.org.uk/main.html
  Click on 'Book Shop'. Includes a few monumental inscriptions

Bosham
- Inscriptions from Holy Trinity, Bosham
  www.towball.freewire.co.uk/inscr__2.htm
  Selected inscriptions

Rottingdean
- Rottingdean Churchyard, Brighton, East Sussex, England
  www.interment.net/data/eng/eastsussex/roddingdean.htm

Warwickshire

Cemeteries
- Warwickshire Cemeteries and Crematoria
  www.genuki.org.uk/big/eng/WAR/deloyd/warcem.htm

Web Page Collections
- Monumental Inscriptions (MIs) of Warwickshire sold by the Birmingham and Midland Society for Genealogy and Heraldry
  www.hunimex.com/warwick/mi/
  Surnames lists from published fiche for many places, listed individually below

Publications
- B.M.S.G.H. Bookshop: Warwickshire
  www.bmsgh.org/bookshop/warw/wa__a.html
  Lists parish registers and monumental inscriptions in book and fiche formats

- Coventry Family History Society Bookshop. Monumental Inscriptions
  www.covfhs.org/
  Click on 'Book Shop' and 'Inscriptions'

Brasses
- Monumental Brass Rubbings for England: Warwickshire
  www.ashmol.co.uk/ash/departments/antiquities/brass/
  Click on 'Catalogue' and county. In the Ashmolean Museum, Oxford

- Warwickshire
  www.mbs-brasses.co.uk/Warwickshire.htm
  Bibliography of monumental brasses

Acocks Green
- Monumental Inscriptions for Acocks Green, St. Mary's
  www.hunimex.com/warwick/mi/mi__brum__acocks__g.html
  List of surnames on fiche no. 1038, available from the Birmingham and Midland Society for Genealogy & Heraldry

Alcester

- Monumental Inscriptions for Alcester, St. Nicholas Church and Alcester Baptist Church
  www.hunimex.com/warwick/mi/mi__alcest.html
  List of surnames on fiche no. 1001, available from the Birmingham & Midland Society for Genealogy & Heraldry

Alderminster

- Monumental Inscriptions for Alderminster, St Mary & The Holy Cross Church
  www.hunimex.com/warwick/mi/mi__alderm.html
  List of surnames on fiche no. 1002, available from the Birmingham and Midland Society for Genealogy & Heraldry

Allesley

- Monumental Inscriptions for Allesley, All Saints Church
  www.hunimex.com/warwick/mi/mi__allas.html
  List of surnames on fiche no. 1003, available from the Birmingham and Midland Society for Genealogy & Heraldry

Alveston

- Monumental Inscriptions for Alveston, St. James'
  www.hunimex.com/warwick/mi/mi__alveston.html
  List of surnames on fiche no. 1004, available from the Birmingham and Midland Society for Genealogy & Heraldry

Ansley

- Monumental Inscriptions for Ansley, St Laurence Church
  www.hunimex.com/warwick/mi/mi__ansley.html
  Lit of surnames on fiche no. 1005, available from the Birmingham and Midland Society for Genealogy & Heraldry

Arley

- Monumental Inscriptions for Arley - New & Old churches
  www.hunimex.com/warwick/mi/mi__arley.html
  List of surnames on fiche no. 1006, available from the Birmingham and Midland Society for Genealogy & Heraldry

Arrow

- Monumental Inscriptions for Arrow, Holy Trinity and Weethley, St James
  www.hunimex.com/warwick/mi/mi__arrow.html
  List of surnames on fiche no. 1007, available from the Birmingham and Midland Society for Genealogy & Heraldry

Ashow

- Monumental Inscriptions for Ashow Church of the Assumption of our Lady
  www.hunimex.com/warwick/mi/mi__ashow.html
  List of surnames on fiche no. 1008, available from the Birmingham and Midland Society for Genealogy & Heraldry

Astley

- Monumental Inscriptions for Astley, Church of the St. Mary the Virgin
  www.hunimex.com/warwick/mi/mi__astley.html
  List of surnames on fiche no. 1009, available from the Birmingham & Midland Society for Genealogy & Heraldry

Aston

- Monumental Inscriptions for Aston, Birmingham; St. Peter & St. Paul
  www.hunimex.com/warwick/mi/mi__aston__pp__long.html
  List of surnames on fiche no. 1039, available from the Birmingham and Midland Society for Genealogy & Heraldry

Aston Cantlow

- Monumental Inscriptions for Aston Cantlow, Church of St John the Baptist
  www.hunimex.com/warwick/mi/mi__aston__cant.html
  List of surnames on fiche no. 1010, available from the Birmingham and Midland Society for Genealogy & Heraldry

Atherstone

- Monumental Inscriptions for Atherstone Methodist Chapel
  www.hunimex.com/warwick/mi/mi__athmc.html
  List of surnames on fiche no. 1011, available from the Birmingham and Midland Society for Genealogy & Heraldry

- Monumental Inscriptions for Atherstone United Reform Church
  www.hunimex.com/warwick/mi/mi__athref.html
  List of surnames on fiche no. 1012, available from the Birmingham and Midland Society for Genealogy & Heraldry

- Monumental Inscriptions for Wood End, Atherstone - St. Michael's
  www.hunimex.com/warwick/mi/mi__athwe.html
  List of surnames on fiche no. 1013, available from the Birmingham and Midland Society for Genealogy & Heraldry

Atherstone Hurley
- Monumental Inscriptions for Atherstone Hurley Church of The Resurrection & Wood End Churchyard
  www.hunimex.com/warwick/mi/mi__atherst__hur.html
  List of surnames on fiche no. 1014, available from the Birmingham and Midland Society for Genealogy & Heraldry

Atherstone on Stour
- Monumental Inscriptions for Atherstone on Stour, St Mary's Church
  www.hunimex.com/warwick/mi/mi__atherst.html
  List of surnames on fiche no. 1015, available from the Birmingham and Midland Society for Genealogy & Heraldry

Attleborough
- Monumental Inscriptions for Attleborough, Holy Trinity Church
  www.hunimex.com/warwick/mi/mi__attleb.html
  List of surnames on fiche no. 1016, available from the Birmingham and Midland Society for Genealogy & Heraldry

Austrey
- Monumental Inscriptions for Austrey, St Nicholas' Church
  www.hunimex.com/warwick/mi/mi__austrey.html
  List of surnames on fiche no. 1017, available from the Birmingham and Midland Society for Genealogy & Heraldry

Avon Dassett
- Monumental Inscriptions for Avon Dassett, St Joseph's RC Church & St John the Baptist Church
  www.hunimex.com/warwick/mi/mi__avondas.html
  List of surnames on fiche no. 1018, available from the Birmingham and Midland Society for Genealogy & Heraldry

Baddesley Clinton
- Monumental Inscriptions for Baddesley Clinton, St Francis of Assisi RC Church
  www.hunimex.com/warwick/mi/mi__badclnt.html
  List of surnames on fiche no. 1019, available from the Birmingham and Midland Society for Genealogy & Heraldry

Baddesley Ensor
- Monumental Inscriptions for Baddesley Ensor, St. Nicholas Church
  www.hunimex.com/warwick/mi/mi__bad__ensor.html
  List of surnames on fiche no. 1020, available from the Birmingham and Midland Society for Genealogy & Heraldry

Baginton
- Monumental Inscriptions for Baginton, St. John the Baptist
  www.hunimex.com/warwick/mi/mi__bagin.html
  List of surnames on fiche no. 1021, available from the Birmingham and Midland Society for Genealogy & Heraldry

Barcheston
- Monumental Inscriptions for Barcheston, St. Martin
  www.hunimex.com/warwick/mi/mi__barch.html
  List of surnames on fiche no. 1022, available from the Birmingham and Midland Society for Genealogy & Heraldry

Barford
- Monumental inscriptions for Barford, St. Peter
  www.hunimex.com/warwick/mi/mi__barford.html
  List of surnames on fiche no. 1023, available from the Birmingham & Midland Society for Genealogy & Heraldry

Barston
- Monumental Inscriptions for Barston, St. Swithun's
  www.hunimex.com/warwick/mi/mi__barston.html
  List of surnames on fiche no. 1024, available from the Birmingham and Midland Society for Genealogy & Heraldry

Bartley Green
- Monumental Inscriptions for Bartley Green, St. Michael & All Saints
  www.hunimex.com/warwick/mi/mi__bartleygreen.html
  List of surnames on fiche no. 1040, available from the Birmingham and Midland Society for Genealogy & Heraldry

Barton on the Heath

- Monumental Inscriptions for Barton on the Heath, St. Lawrence
  www.hunimex.com/warwick/mi/mi__barton.html
  List of surnames on fiche no 1023, available from the Birmingham and Midland Society for Genealogy & Heraldry

Bascote Heath

See Southam

Baxterley

- Monumental Inscriptions for Baxterley Parish Church
  www.hunimex.com/warwick/mi/mi__baxterley.html
  List of surnames on fiche no. 1027, available from the Birmingham and Midland Society for Genealogy & Heraldry

Bearley

- Monumental Inscriptions for Bearley, St. Mary the Virgin
  www.hunimex.com/warwick/mi/mi__bearley.html
  List of surnames on fiche no. 1028, available from the Birmingham and Midland Society for Genealogy & Heraldry

Bedworth

- Monumental Inscriptions for Bedworth, All Saints church, Independent & Zionist chapel
  www.hunimex.com/warwick/mi/mi__bedas.html
  List of surnames on fiche no. 1028, available from the Birmingham and Midland Society for Genealogy & Heraldry

Bentley

- Monumental Inscriptions for Bentley, St. John's Churchyard
  www.hunimex.com/warwick/mi/mi__bentley.html
  List of surnames on fiche no. 1030, available from the Birmingham and Midland Society for Genealogy & Heraldry

Berkswell

- Monumental Inscriptions for Berkswell, St. John the Baptist
  www.hunimex.com/warwick/mi/mi__berks.html
  List of surnames on fiche no. 1031, available from the Birmingham and Midland Society for Genealogy & Heraldry

Binton

- Monumental Inscriptions for Binton, St. Peter
  www.hunimex.com/warwick/mi/mi__binton.html
  List of surnames on fiche no. 1036, available from the Birmingham and Midland Society for Genealogy & Heraldry

Birdingbury

- Monumental Inscriptions for Birdingbury, St. Leonards
  www.hunimex.com/warwick/mi/mi__birdingbury.html
  List of surnames on fiche no. 1037, available from the Birmingham and Midland Society for Genealogy & Heraldry

Birmingham

- Monumental Inscriptions for Birmingham, St. Martin's Church, Park Street, St. Bartholomew's Church and Zion Baptist Church
  www.hunimex.com/warwick/mi/mi__brum__zion.html
  List of surnames on fiche no. 1061, available from the Birmingham and Midland Society for Genealogy & Heraldry

- Monumental Inscriptions for Birmingham, Whittall Street, St. Mary
  www.hunimex.com/warwick/mi/mi__brum__whittall.html
  List of surnames on fiche no. 1071, available from the Birmingham and Midland Society for Genealogy & Heraldry

- Monumental Inscriptions for Birmingham General Hospital
  www.hunimex.com/warwick/mi/mi__brum__g__hosp.html
  List of surnames on fiche no. 1050, available from the Birmingham and Midland Society for Genealogy & Heraldry

Bishop's Itchington

- Monumental Inscriptions for Bishops Itchington, St. Michael's
  www.hunimex.com/warwick/mi/mi__bisitc.html
  List of surnames on fiche no. 1072, available from the Birmingham and Midland Society for Genealogy & Heraldry

Bishops Tachbrook

- Monumental Inscriptions for Bishop's Tachbrook, St Chad's
  www.hunimex.com/warwick/mi/mi__bishtac.html
  List of surnames on fiche no. 1073, available from the Birmingham and Midland Society for Genealogy & Heraldry

Bordesley

- Monumental Inscriptions for Bordesley, Holy Trinity
  www.hunimex.com/warwick/mi/mi__bordesley.html
  List of surnames on fiche no. 1042, available from the Birmingham and Midland Society for Genealogy & Heraldry

Brailes

- Monumental Inscriptions for Brailes, St. George's
  www.hunimex.com/warwick/mi/mi__brail.html
  List of surnames on fiche no. 1076, available from the Birmingham and Midland Society for Genealogy & Heraldry

Brinklow

- Monumental Inscriptions for Brinklow, St. John the Baptist
  www.hunimex.com/warwick/mi/mi__brink.html
  List of surnames on fiche no. 1077, available from the Birmingham and Midland Society for Genealogy & Heraldry

Bubbenhall

- Monumental Inscriptions for Bubbenhall, St. Giles
  www.hunimex.com/warwick/mi/mi__bubben.html
  List of surnames on fiche no. 1078, available from the Birmingham and Midland Society for Genealogy & Heraldry

Burton Hastings

- Monumental Inscriptions for Burton Hastings, St. Botolph
  www.hunimex.com/warwick/mi/mi__burton.h.html
  List of surnames on fiche no. 1082, available from the Birmingham and Midland Society for Genealogy & Heraldry

Chilvers Coton

- Monumental Inscriptions for Chilvers Coton, All Saints
  www.hunimex.com/warwick/mi/mi__chilcot__sht.html
  List of surnames on fiche no. 1089, available from the Birmingham and Midland Society for Genealogy & Heraldry

- Monumental Inscriptions for Chilvers Coton, All Saints: Index to Kerbs Removed in 1987
  www.hunimex.com/warwick/mi/mi__chilcot__rem.html
  List of surnames on fiche no. 1089, available from the Birmingham and Midland Society for Genealogy & Heraldry

Church Lawford

- Monumental Inscriptions for Church Lawford, St Peter's
  www.hunimex.com/warwick/mi/mi__chlaw.html
  List of surnames on fiche no. 1090, available from the Birmingham and Midland Society for Genealogy & Heraldry

Copston Magna

See Withybrook

Coventry

- Monumental Inscriptions for Coventry, Holy Trinity
  www.hunimex.com/warwick/mi/mi__covht.html
  List of surnames on fiche no. 1102, available from the Birmingham and Midland Society for Genealogy & Heraldry

- Monumental Inscriptions for Coventry Independent Churches
  www.hunimex.com/warwick/mi/mi__coventry__ind.html
  List of surnames on fiche no. 1103, available from the Birmingham and Midland Society for Genealogy & Heraldry

- Monumental Inscriptions for Coventry St John the Baptist
  www.hunimex.com/warwick/mi/mi__covjtb.html
  List of surnames on fiche no. 1104, available from the Birmingham and Midland Society for Genealogy & Heraldry

- Monumental Inscriptions for Coventry West Orchard Chapel
  www.hunimex.com/warwick/mi/mi__coventry__w__orch.html
  List of surnames on fiche no. 1107, available from the Birmingham and Midland Society for Genealogy & Heraldry

Cubbington

- Monumental Inscriptions for Cubbington, St. Mary
  www.hunimex.com/warwick/mi/mi__cubb.html
  List of surnames on fiche no. 1109, available from the Birmingham and Midland Society for Genealogy & Heraldry

Dunchurch

- Monumental Inscriptions for Dunchurch, St. Peter's
  www.hunimex.com/warwick/mi/mi__dunch.html
  List of surnames on fiche no. 1114, available from the Birmingham and Midland Society for Genealogy & Heraldry

- Monumental Inscriptions for Dunchurch Baptist Church
  www.hunimex.com/warwick/mi/mi__dunbp.html
  List of surnames on fiche no. 1113, available from the Birmingham and Midland Society for Genealogy & Heraldry

Edgbaston
- Monumental Inscriptions for Edgbaston, St. Augustine's
  www.hunimex.com/warwick/mi/mi__edgbaston__a.html
  List of surnames on fiche no. 1045, available from the Birmingham and Midland Society for Genealogy & Heraldry

Erdington
- Monumental Inscriptions for Erdington Congregational Church
  www.hunimex.com/warwick/mi/mi__erdington__c.html
  List of surnames on fiche no. 1048, available from the Birmingham and Midland Society for Genealogy & Heraldry

Exhall
- Monumental Inscriptions for Exhall, St. Giles
  www.hunimex.com/warwick/mi/mi__exhl.html
  List of surnames on fiche no. 1120, available from the Birmingham and Midland Society for Genealogy & Heraldry

Farnborough
- Monumental Inscriptions for Farnborough, St. Botolph
  www.hunimex.com/warwick/mi/mi__farnborough.html
  List of surnames on fiche no. 1122, available from the Birmingham and Midland Society for Genealogy & Heraldry

Flecknoe
- Monumental Inscriptions for Flecknoe, St Mark's and Willoughby St Nicholas
  www.hunimex.com/warwick/mi/mi__fleck.html
  List of surnames on fiche no. 1124, available from the Birmingham and Midland Society for Genealogy & Heraldry

Frankton
- Monumental Inscriptions for Frankton, St. Nicholas
  www.hunimex.com/warwick/mi/mi__frank.html
  List of surnames on fiche no. 1126, available from the Birmingham and Midland Society for Genealogy & Heraldry

Grandborough
- Monumental Inscriptions for Grandborough, St. Peter's
  www.hunimex.com/warwick/mi/mi__grand.html
  List of surnames on fiche no. 1128, available from the Birmingham and Midland Society for Genealogy & Heraldry

Handsworth
- Monumental Inscriptions for Handsworth, Birmingham St. Andrews & Congregational Chapel, Union Row
  www.hunimex.com/warwick/mi/mi__handsworth__a.html
  List of surnames on fiche no. 1052, available from the Birmingham and Midland Society for Genealogy & Heraldry

Harbury
- Monumental Inscriptions for Harbury, All Saints
  www.hunimex.com/warwick/mi/mi__hamb.html
  List of surnames on fiche no. 1137, available from the Birmingham and Midland Society for Genealogy & Heraldry

Hockley
- Monumental Inscriptions for Hockley, All Saints
  www.hunimex.com/warwick/mi/mi__hockley__as.html
  List of surnames on fiche no. 1056, available from the Birmingham and Midland Society for Genealogy & Heraldry

Hunningham
- Monumental Inscriptions for Hunningham, St. Margaret's
  www.hunimex.com/warwick/mi/mi__hunning.html
  List of surnames on fiche no. 1145, available from the Birmingham and Midland Society for Genealogy & Heraldry

Kenilworth
- Monumental Inscriptions for Kenilworth, St. Austin's R.C.Church
  www.hunimex.com/warwick/mi/mi__kenrc.html
  List of surnames on fiche no. 1148, available from the Birmingham and Midland Society for Genealogy & Heraldry

Kings Heath
- Monumental Inscriptions for Birmingham, Kings Heath All Saints
  www.hunimex.com/warwick/mi/mi__kings__heath.html
  List of surnames on fiche no. 1058, available from the Birmingham and Midland Society for Genealogy & Heraldry

Ladbroke

- Monumental Inscriptions for Ladbroke, All Saints Church
  www.hunimex.com/warwick/mi/mi__ladas.html
  List of surnames on fiche no. 1152, available from the Birmingham and Midland Society for Genealogy & Heraldry

Leamington Hastings

- Monumental Inscriptions for Leamington Hastings, All Saints
  www.hunimex.com/warwick/mi/mi__leamh.html
  List of surnames on fiche no. 1156, available from the Birmingham and Midland Society for Genealogy & Heraldry

Leamington Spa

- Monumental Inscriptions for the Churches of Leamington Spa
  www.hunimex.com/warwick/mi/mi__leamch.html
  List of surnames on fiche no. 1158, available from the Birmingham and Midland Society for Genealogy & Heraldry

- Monumental Inscriptions for Leamington Spa, All Saints
  www.hunimex.com/warwick/mi/mi__leamsp.html
  List of surnames on fiche no. 1157, available from the Birmingham and Midland Society for Genealogy & Heraldry

- Monumental Inscriptions for Leamington Spa, Brunswick Street Cemetery
  www.hunimex.com/warwick/mi/mi__lspa.bruns.html
  List of surnames on fiche no. 1155, available from the Birmingham and Midland Society for Genealogy & Heraldry

Leek Wooton

- Monumental Inscriptions for Leek Wooton, All Saints
  www.hunimex.com/warwick/mi/mi__leekw.html
  List of surnames on fiche no. 1159, available from the Birmingham and Midland Society for Genealogy & Heraldry

Long Itchington

- Monumental Inscriptions for Long Itchington, Holy Trinity
  www.hunimex.com/warwick/mi/mi__lgitch.html
  List of surnames on fiche no. 1164, available from the Birmingham and Midland Society for Genealogy & Heraldry

Mancetter

- Monumental Inscriptions for Mancetter, St Peter's Church
  www.hunimex.com/warwick/mi/mi__mancet.html
  List of surnames on fiche no. 1169, available from the Birmingham and Midland Society for Genealogy & Heraldry

Monks Kirby

- Monumental Inscriptions for Monks Kirby, St Editha
  www.hunimex.com/warwick/mi/mi__mkste.html
  List of surnames on fiche no. 1176, available from the Birmingham and Midland Society for Genealogy & Heraldry

- Monumental Inscriptions for Monks Kirby Roman Catholic Church
  www.hunimex.com/warwick/mi/mi__mkrc.html
  List of surnames on fiche no. 1176, available from the Birmingham and Midland Society for Genealogy & Heraldry

Napton

- Monumental Inscriptions for Napton, St. Lawrence
  www.hunimex.com/warwick/mi/mi__napt.html
  List of surnames on fiche no. 1179, available from the Birmingham and Midland Society for Genealogy & Heraldry

Newbold on Avon

- Monumental Inscriptions for Newbold-on-Avon, St Botolph's Church
  www.hunimex.com/warwick/mi/mi__nb__avon.html
  List of surnames on fiche no. 1181, available from the Birmingham and Midland Society for Genealogy & Heraldry

Nuneaton

- Monumental Inscriptions for Nuneaton, Our Lady of the Angels
  www.hunimex.com/warwick/mi/mi__nuneaton__l.html
  List of surnames on fiche no. 1186, available from the Birmingham and Midland Society for Genealogy & Heraldry

- Monumental Inscriptions for Nuneaton, St. Nicholas
  www.hunimex.com/warwick/mi/mi__nuneaton.n.html
  List of surnames on fiche no. 1187, available from the Birmingham and Midland Society for Genealogy & Heraldry

Offchurch
- Monumental Inscriptions for Offchurch, St Gregory
  www.hunimex.com/warwick/mi/mi__offch.html
  List of surnames on fiche no. 1188, available from the Birmingham and Midland Society for Genealogy & Heraldry

Old Milverton
- Monumental Inscriptions for Old Milverton, St James
  www.hunimex.com/warwick/mi/mi__oldmi.html
  List of surnames on fiche no. 1189, available from the Birmingham and Midland Society for Genealogy & Heraldry

Priors Hardwick
- Monumental Inscriptions for Priors Hardwick, St. Mary's
  www.hunimex.com/warwick/mi/mi__priors_h.html
  List of surnames on fiche no. 1201, available from theBirmingham and Midland Society for Genealogy & Heraldry

Radford Semele
- Monumental Inscriptions for Radford Semele, St. Nicholas
  www.hunimex.com/warwick/mi/mi__radfs.html
  List of surnames on fiche no. 1203, available from the Birmingham and Midland Society for Genealogy & Heraldry

Radway
- Monumental Inscriptions for Radway, St. Peter's
  www.hunimex.com/warwick/mi/mi__radway.html
  List of surnames on fiche no. 1204, available from the Birmingham and Midland Society for Genealogy & Heraldry

Rowington
- Monumental Inscriptions for Rowington, St. Lawrence
  www.hunimex.com/warwick/mi/mi__rowington.html
  List of surnames on fiche no. 1206, available from the Birmingham and Midland Society for Genealogy & Heraldry

Rugby
- Rugby Cemeteries & Crematoria
  ukburials-cremations.co.uk/rugby__cem__crem.htm
  Brief list

- Monumental Inscriptions for Rugby, St. Matthew, St. Andrew & St. Oswald's
  www.hunimex.com/warwick/mi/mi__rugby__mao.html
  List of surnames on fiche no. 1207, available from the Birmingham and Midland Society for Genealogy & Heraldry

- Monumental Inscriptions for Rugby, Croop Hill
  www.hunimex.com/warwick/mi/mi__rugby__croop.html
  List of surnames on fiche no. 1208, available from the Birmingham and Midland Society for Genealogy & Heraldry

- Monumental Inscriptions for Rugby, St Marie's RC
  www.hunimex.com/warwick/mi/mi__rugby__rc.html
  List of surnames on fiche no. 1209, available from the Birmingham and Midland Society for Genealogy & Heraldry

Ryton on Dunsmore
- Monumental Inscriptions for Ryton-on-Dunsmore, St Leonard's
  www.hunimex.com/warwick/mi/mi__ryton.html
  List of surnames on fiche no. 1210, available from the Birmingham and Midland Society for Genealogy & Heraldry

Salford Priors
- Monumental Inscriptions for Salford Priors, St. Matthews
  www.hunimex.com/warwick/mi/mi__salford.p.html
  List of surnames on fiche no. 1211, available from the Birmingham and Midland Society for Genealogy & Heraldry

Saltley
- Monumental Inscriptions for Birmingham, Saltley St. Saviour's
  www.hunimex.com/warwick/mi/mi__brum__salt.html
  List of surnames on fiche no. 1066, available from the Birmingham and Midland Society for Genealogy & Heraldry

Sherbourne
- Monumental Inscriptions for Sherbourne, All Saints
  www.hunimex.com/warwick/mi/mi__sherbourne.html
  List of surnames on fiche no. 1213, available from the Birmingham and Midland Society for Genealogy & Heraldry

Shilton

- Monumental Inscriptions for Shilton, St. Andrew's Church
  www.hunimex.com/warwick/mi/mi__shilt.html
  List of surnames onfiche no. 1214, available from the Birmingham and Midland Society for Gene4alogy & Heraldry

Shotteswell

- Monumental Inscriptions for Shotteswell, St. Lawrence
  www.hunimex.com/warwick/mi/mi__shotteswell.html
  List of surnames on fiche no. 1216, available from the Birmingham and Midland Society for Genealogy & Heraldry

Shustoke

- Monumental Inscriptions for Shustoke, St. Cuthbert's
  www.hunimex.com/warwick/mi/mi__shustoke.html
  List of surnames on fiche no. 1218, available from the Birmingham and Midland Society for Genealogy & Heraldry

Snittersfield

- Monumental Inscriptions for Snittersfield, St. James the Great
  www.hunimex.com/warwick/mi/mi__snittersfield.html
  List of surnames on fiche no. 1219, available from the Birmingham and Midland Society for Genealogy & Heraldry

Southam

- Monumental Inscriptions for Southam, St James' Church
  www.hunimex.com/warwick/mi/mi__southam.html
  List of surnames on fiche no. 1221, available from the Birmingham and Midland Society for Genealogy & Heraldry

- Monumental Inscriptions for Southam, Bascote Heath Churchyard
  www.hunimex.com/warwick/mi/mi__bascote.html
  List of surnames on fiche no. 1026, available from the Birmingham and Midland Society for Genealogy & Heraldry

Stivichall

- Monumental Inscriptions for Styvechale (Coventry) St James
  www.hunimex.com/warwick/mi/mi__covssj.html
  List of surnames on fiche no. 1105, available from the Birmingham and Midland Society for Genealogy & Heraldry

Stockingford

- Monumental Inscriptions for Stockingford, St. Paul's
  www.hunimex.com/warwick/mi/mi__stockingford.html
  List of surnames on fiche no. 1222, available from the Birmingham and Midland Society for Genealogy & Heraldry

Stockton

- Monumental Inscriptions for Stockton, St Michael's
  www.hunimex.com/warwick/mi/mi__stckn.html
  List of surnames on fiche no. 1223, available from the Birmingham and Midland Society for Genealogy & Heraldry

Stoneleigh

- Monumental Inscriptions for Stoneleigh, St. Mary's
  www.hunimex.com/warwick/mi/mi__stone.html
  List of surnames on fiche no. 1224, available from the Birmingham and Midland Society for Genealogy & Heraldry

Stretton on the Fosse

- Monumental Inscriptions for Stretton on the Fosse, St Peter's
  www.hunimex.com/warwick/mi/mi__stretton__on.html
  List of surnames on fiche no. 1225, available from the Birmingham and Midland Society for Genealogy & Heraldry

- Monumental Inscriptions for Stretton Under Fosse Chapel
  www.hunimex.com/warwick/mi/mi__stretton__under.html
  List of surnames on fiche no. 1227, available from the Birmingham and Midland Society for Genealogy & Heraldry

Studley

- Monumental Inscriptions for Studley, St. Mary the Virgin, Cemetery & Baptist Church
  www.hunimex.com/warwick/mi/mi__studley__b__sht.html
  List of surnames on fiche no. 1228, available from the Birmingham and Midland Society for Genealogy & Heraldry

Tanworth in Arden

- Monumental Inscriptions for Tanworth in Arden, St. Mary Magdalene Church
  www.hunimex.com/warwick/mi/mi__tanwth.html
  List of surnames on fiche no. 1231, available from the Birmingham and Midland Society for Genealogy & Heraldry

Temple Balsall

- Monumental Inscriptions for Temple Balsall, St. Mary the Virgin church & cemetery
  www.hunimex.com/warwick/mi/mi__temple__balsall.html
  List of surnames on fiche no. 1232, available from the Birmingham and Midland Society for Genealogy & Heraldry

Tysoe

- Monumental Inscriptions for Tysoe, Church of the Assumption of the Blessed Virgin Mary
  www.hunimex.com/warwick/mi/mi__tysoe.html
  List of surnames on fiche no. 1234, available from the Birmingham and Midland Society for Genealogy & Heraldry

Ufton

- Monumental Inscriptions for Ufton, St. Michael's and All Angels
  www.hunimex.com/warwick/mi/mi__ufton.html
  List of surnames on fiche no. 1235, available from the Birmingham and Midland Society for Genealogy & Heraldry

Ullenhall

- Monumental Inscriptions for Ullenhall, St. Mary the Virgin Church and Chapel
  www.hunimex.com/warwick/mi/mi__ullenhall.html
  List of surnames on fiche no. 1236, available from the Birmingham and Midland Society for Genealogy & Heraldry

Umberslade

- Monumental Inscriptions for Umberslade Baptist Chapel
  www.hunimex.com/warwick/mi/mi__umbers.html
  List of surnames on fiche no. 1237, available from the Birmingham and Midland Society for Genealogy & Heraldry

Walmley

- Monumental Inscriptions for Walmley, St. John the Evangelist
  www.hunimex.com/warwick/mi/mi__walmley.html
  List of surnames on fiche no. 1238, available from the Birmingham and Midland Society for Genealogy & Heraldry

Walsgrave on Sowe

- Monumental Inscriptions for Walsgrave-on-Sowe, St Mary's Church
  www.hunimex.com/warwick/mi/mi__walsg.html
  List of surnames on fiche no. 1239, available from the Birmingham and Midland Society for Genealogy & Heraldry

Walton D'Eivile

- Monumental Inscriptions for Walton D'Eivile, St James'
  www.hunimex.com/warwick/mi/mi__walton__d.html
  List of surnames on fiche no. 1240, available from the Birmingham and Midland Society for Genealogy & Heraldry

Wappenbury

- Monumental Inscriptions for Wappenbury, St. Ann's R.C. Church
  www.hunimex.com/warwick/mi/mi__wappenbury__a.html
  List of surnames on fiche no. 1241, available from the Birmingham and Midland Society for Genealogy & Heraldry

- Monumental Inscriptions for Wappenbury, St John the Baptist
  www.hunimex.com/warwick/mi/mi__wappenbury__j.html
  List of surnames on fiche no. 1242, available from the Birmingham and Midland Society for Genealogy & Heraldry

Warton

- Monumental Inscriptions for Warton, Holy Trinity
  www.hunimex.com/warwick/mi/mi__warton.html
  List of surnames on fiche no. 1244, available from the Birmingham and Midland Society for Genealogy & Heraldry

Warwick

- Monumental Inscriptions for Warwick, The Cemetery - Birmingham Road
  www.hunimex.com/warwick/mi/mi__warwick__cem.html
  List of surnames on fiche no. 1268, available from the Birmingham and Midland Society for Genealogy & Heraldry

- Monumental Inscriptions for Warwick, St. Paul's
  www.hunimex.com/warwick/mi/mi__warkp.html
  List of surnames on fiche no. 1245, available from the Birmingham and Midland Society for Genealogy & Heraldry

Wasperton

- Monumental Inscriptions for Wasperton, St. John the Baptist
  www.hunimex.com/warwick/mi/mi__wasperton.html
  List of surnames on fiche no. 1246, available from the Birmingham and Midland Society for Genealogy & Heraldry

Water Orton

- Monumental Inscriptions for Water Orton, S.S. Peter and Paul
  www.hunimex.com/warwick/mi/mi__water__orton.html
  List of surnames on fiche no. 1247, available from the Birmingham and Midland Society for Genealogy & Heraldry

Weddington

- Monumental Inscriptions for Weddington, St. James'
  www.hunimex.com/warwick/mi/mi__weddington.html
  List of surnames on fiche no. 1248, available from the Birmingham and Midland Society for Genealogy & Heraldry

Weethley

See Arrow

Weston on Avon

- Monumental Inscriptions for Weston on Avon, All Saints
  www.hunimex.com/warwick/mi/mi__weston.html
  List of surnames on fiche no. 1250, available from the Birmingham and Midland Society for Genealogy & Heraldry

Weston under Wetherley

- Monumental Inscriptions for Weston-under-Wetherley
  www.hunimex.com/warwick/mi/mi__westuw.html
  List of surnames on fiche no. 1251, available from the Birmingham and Midland Society for Genealogy & Heraldry

Whichford

- Monumental Inscriptions for Whichford, St. Michael's
  www.hunimex.com/warwick/mi/mi__whichford.html
  List of surnames on fiche no. 1253, available from the Birmingham and Midland Society for Genealogy & Heraldry

Willoughby

See Flecknoe

Wilnecote

- Monumental Inscriptions for Wilnecote Old Cemetery, Holy Trinity Church
  www.hunimex.com/warwick/mi/mi__wilnecote.html
  List of surnames on fiche no. 1256, available from the Birmingham and Midland Society for Genealogy & Heraldry

Wishaw

- Monumental Inscriptions for Wishaw, St. Chad
  www.hunimex.com/warwick/mi/mi__wishaw.html
  List of surnames on fiche no. 1257, available from the Birmingham and Midland Society for Genealogy & Heraldry

Withybrook

- Monumental Inscriptions for Withybrook, All Saints, and Copston Magna, St John
  www.hunimex.com/warwick/mi/mi__withybrook.html
  List of surnames on fiche no. 1258, available from the Birmingham and Midland Society for Genealogy & Heraldry

Wolfhamcote

- Monumental Inscriptions for Wolfhamcote, St Peter's
  www.hunimex.com/warwick/mi/mi__wolfh.html
  List of surnames on fiche no. 1259, available from the Birmingham and Midland Society for Genealogy & Heraldry

Wolverton

- Monumental Inscriptions for Wolverton, St. Mary The Virgin
  www.hunimex.com/warwick/mi/mi__wolverton.html
  List of surnames on fiche no. 1261, available from the Birmingham and Midland Society for Genealogy & Heraldry

Wolvey

- Monumental Inscriptions for Wolvey, St. John the Baptist
  www.hunimex.com/warwick/mi/mi__wolvey.html
  List of surnames on fiche no. 1262, available from the Birmingham and Midland Society for Genealogy & Heraldry

Wootton Wawen

- Monumental Inscriptions for Wootton Wawen, St. Peter's
  www.hunimex.com/warwick/mi/mi__wwawen-peter.html
  List of surnames on fiche no. 1264, available from the Birmingham and Midland Society for Genealogy & Heraldry

- Monumental Inscriptions for Wootton Wawen, Our Lady & St. Benedict R.C.
  www.hunimex.com/warwick/mi/mi__wwawen-bened.html
  List of surnames on fiche no. 1263, available from the Birmingham and Midland Society for Geneallgy & Heraldry

Wormleighton
- Monumental Inscriptions for Wormleighton, St. Peter's
  www.hunimex.com/warwick/mi/mi__wormleighton.html
  List of surnames on fiche no. 1265, available from the Birmingham and Midland Society for Genealogy & Heraldry

Wroxall
- Monumental Inscriptions for Wroxall, St. Leonard's
  www.hunimex.com/warwick/mi/mi__wrox.html
  List of surnames on fiche no. 1266, available from the Birmingham and Midland Soceity for Genealogy & Heraldry

Wyken
- Monumental Inscriptions for Wyken, St. Mary Magdalene with the Risen Christ
  www.hunimex.com/warwick/mi/mi__wyken.html
  List of surnames on fiche no. 1267, available from the Birmingham and Midland Society for Genealogy & Heraldry

Westmorland

Brasses
- [Westmorland Monumental Brasses]
  home.clara.net/williamlack/indices/westm.htm
  Index to a book

- Monumental Brass Rubbings for England: Westmorland
  www.ashmol.co.uk/ash/departments/antiquities/brass/
  Click on 'Catalogue' and county. In the Ashmolean Museum, Oxford

- Westmorland
  www.mbs-brasses.co.uk/Westmoreland.htm
  Bibliography of monumental brasses

Ravenstonedale
- St. Oswalds Gravestone Index, Ravenstonedale, Kirkby Stephen, Cumbria
  www.ravenstonedale.org/general/churches/oswalds/graves1.htm

Wiltshire

Web Page Collections

- Duncan, Mandy and Michelle's Website
  www.oodwooc.f9.co.uk
  Collection of web-pages containing photographs of Wiltshire
  monumental inscriptions. Indexes are linked to on this page; pages for
  particular places are separately listed below

- Wishful Thinking's GENUKI: Wiltshire Pages: Memorial Inscription
  Collection
  www.wishful-thinking.org.uk/genuki/WIL/MIs.html

Brasses

- Wiltshire
  www.mbs-brasses.co.uk/wiltshire.htm
  Bibliography of monumental brasses

All Cannings

- All Saints, All Cannings, Wiltshire
  www.oodwooc.f9.co.uk/ph__allcannings.htm
  Photographs of inscriptions

Amesbury

- Amesbury, Wiltshire
  www.oodwooc.f9.co.uk/ph__amesbury.htm
  Photographs of inscriptions

Ashton Keynes

- Holy Cross, Ashton Keynes, Wiltshire
  www.oodwooc.f9.co.uk/ph__ak.htm
  Photographs of inscriptions

Avebury

- Congregational Chapel, Avebury, Wiltshire
  www.oodwooc.f9.co.uk/ph__avebury.htm
  Photographs of inscriptions

Baydon

- St. Nicholas, Baydon, Wiltshire
  www.oodwooc.f9.co.uk/ph__baydon.htm
  Photographs of inscriptions

Berwick Bassett

- St. Nicholas, Berwick Bassett, Wiltshire
  www.oodwooc.f9.co.uk/ph__berbassett.htm
  Photographs of inscriptions

Bishops Cannings

- St. Mary the Virgin, Bishops Cannings, Wiltshire
  www.oodwooc.f9.co.uk/ph__bishopcan.htm
  Photographs of inscriptions

Bishopstone

- St. Mary the Virgin, Bishopstone, Wiltshire
  www.oodwooc.f9.co.uk/ph__bishswi.htm
  Photographs of inscriptions

Blunsdon St. Andrew

- St. Andrew, Blunsdon St. Andrew, Wiltshire
  www.oodwooc.f9.co.uk/ph__blunsta.htm
  Photographs of inscriptions

Brinkworth

- St. Michael's and All Angels, Brinkworth, Wiltshire
  www.oodwooc.f9.co.uk/ph__brinkworth.htm
  Photographs of inscriptions

Broad Blunsdon

- St. Leonard's, Broad Blunsdon, Wiltshire
  www.oodwooc.f9.co.uk/ph__brblunsdon.htm
  Photographs of inscriptions

Broad Hinton

- St. Peter ad Vincular, Broad Hinton, Wiltshire
  www.oodwooc.f9.co.uk/ph__broadhinton.htm
  Photographs of inscriptions

Broughton Gifford

- St. Mary the Virgin, Broughton Gifford, Wiltshire
  www.oodwooc.f9.co.uk/ph__BroGif.htm
  Photographs of inscriptions

Burbage

- Burbage Monumental Inscriptions
  www.keble.clara.net/mis.htm

Calne

- Methodist Church at Calne, Wiltshire
  www.oodwooc.f9.co.uk/ph__calne.htm
  Photographs of inscriptions

Castle Eaton

- St. Mary's, Castle Eaton, Wiltshire
  www.oodwooc.f9.co.uk/ph__castleaton.htm
  Photographs of inscriptions

Charlton

- St. John the Baptist, Charlton, Wiltshire
  www.oodwooc.f9.co.uk/ph__charlton.htm
  Photographs of inscriptions

Chilton Foliat

- St. Mary, Chilton Foliat, Wiltshire
  www.oodwooc.f9.co.uk/ph__chiltf.htm
  Photographs of inscriptions

Chiseldon

- Holy Cross, Chiseldon, Wiltshire
  www.oodwooc.f9.co.uk/ph__chiseldon.htm
  Photographs of inscriptions

Christian Malford

- All Saints, Christian Malford, Wiltshire
  www.oodwooc.f9.co.uk/ph__cmalford.htm
  Photographs of inscriptions

Cliffe Pypard

- St. Peter, Clyffe Pypard, Wiltshire
  www.oodwooc.f9.co.uk/ph__cp.htm
  Photographs of inscriptions

Collingbourne Ducis

- St. Andrew, Collingbourne Ducis, Wiltshire
  www.oodwooc.f9.co.uk/ph__collingducis.htm
  Photographs of inscriptions

Compton Bassett

- St. Swithin, Compton Bassett, Wiltshire
  www.oodwooc.f9.co.uk/ph__comptonbas.htm
  Photographs of inscriptions

Corston

- All Saints, Corston, Wiltshire
  www.oodwooc.f9.co.uk/ph__corston.htm
  Photographs of inscriptions

Cricklade

- St. Sampson, Cricklade, Wiltshire
  www.oodwooc.f9.co.uk/ph__cricklade.htm
  Photographs of inscriptions

- Friends of St. Mary's Church, Cricklade, Wiltshire, U.K. Churchyard
  www.tetlow.screaming.net/churchyard.htm
  Monumental inscriptions

Crudwell

- Some Memorial Inscriptions: Crudwell, Wiltshire: All Saints Churchyard
  www.wishful-thinking.org.uk/Genuki/WIL/Crudwell/Mls.html

- All Saints, Crudwell, Wiltshire
  www.oodwooc.f9.co.uk/ph__crud.htm
  Photographs of inscriptions

Dauntsey

- St. James the Great, Dauntsey, Wiltshire
  www.oodwooc.f9.co.uk/ph__daun.htm
  Photographs of inscriptions

Draycot Cerne

- St. James, Draycot Cerne, Wiltshire
  www.oodwooc.f9.co.uk/ph__draycotcerne.htm
  Photographs of inscriptions

Easton Grey
- Easton Grey, Gloucestershire
  www.oodwooc.f9.co.uk/ph__egrey.htm
  Photographs of inscriptions; actually in Wiltshire

Foxley
- Foxley, Wiltshire
  www.oodwooc.f9.co.uk/ph__foxley.htm
  Photgraphs of inscriptions

Fyfield
- St. Nicholas, Fyfield, Wiltshire
  www.oodwooc.f9.co.uk/ph__fyfield.htm
  Photographs of inscriptions

Garsdon
- All Saints, Garsdon, Wiltshire
  www.oodwooc.f9.co.uk/ph__garsdon.htm
  Photographs of inscriptions

Great Bedwyn
- St. Mary the Virgin, Great Bedwyn, Wiltshire
  www.oodwooc.f9.co.uk/ph__greatbedwyn.htm
  Photographs of inscriptions

Great Somerford
- Saint Peter and Paul, Great Somerford, Wiltshire
  www.oodwooc.f9.co.uk/ph__gsom.htm
  Photographs of inscriptions

Grittleton
- St. Mary's, Grittleton, Wiltshire
  www.oodwooc.f9.co.uk/ph__grit.htm
  Photographs of inscriptions

Ham
- Ham, Wiltshire
  www.oodwooc.f9.co.uk/ph__ham.htm
  Photographs of inscriptions

Hankerton
- Holy Cross, Hankerton, Wiltshire
  www.oodwooc.f9.co.uk/ph__hankerton.htm
  Photographs of inscriptions

Hannington
- St. John the Baptist, Hannington, Wiltshire
  www.oodwooc.f9.co.uk/ph__hannington.htm
  Photographs of inscriptions

Highworth
- St. Michael's, Highworth, Wiltshire
  www.oodwooc.f9.co.uk/ph__highworth.htm
  Photographs of inscriptions

Hilperton
- St. Michaels and All Angels, Hilperton, Wiltshire
  www.oodwooc.f9.co.uk/ph__hilperton.htm
  Photographs of inscriptions

Holt
- St. Katharine, Holt, Wiltshire
  www.oodwooc.f9.co.uk/ph__holt.htm
  Photographs of inscriptions

Hullavington
- St. Mary Magdalene, Hullavington, Wiltshire
  www.oodwooc.f9.co.uk/ph__hullavington.htm
  Photographs of inscriptions

Kempsford
- St. Mary the Virgin, Kempsford, Gloucestershire
  www.oodwooc.f9.co.uk/ph__kempsford.htm
  Photographs of inscriptions

Kington St. Michael
- St. Michael and All Angels, Kington St. Michael, Wiltshire
  www.oodwooc.f9.co.uk/ph__kingstm.htm
  Photographs of inscriptions

Latton

- St. John the Baptist, Latton, Wiltshire
  www.oodwooc.f9.co.uk/ph__latton.htm
  Photographs of inscriptions

Lea

- St. Giles, Lea, Wiltshire
  www.oodwooc.f9.co.uk/ph__lea.htm
  Photographs of inscriptions

Leigh

- All Saints, Leigh, Wiltshire
  www.oodwooc.f9.co.uk/ph__leigh.htm
  Photographs of inscriptions

Leigh Delamere

- St. Margaret, Leigh Delamere, Wiltshire
  www.oodwooc.f9.co.uk/ph__LeighD.htm
  Photographs of inscriptions

Liddington

- All Saints, Liddington, Wiltshire
  www.oodwooc.f9.co.uk/ph__liddington.htm
  Photographs of inscriptions

Little Hinton

- St. Swithun, Little Hinton (Parva), Wiltshire
  www.oodwooc.f9.co.uk/ph__lithint.htm
  Photographs of inscriptions

Little Somerford

- St. John the Baptist, Little Somerford, Wiltshire
  www.oodwooc.f9.co.uk/ph__lsom.htm
  Photographs of inscriptions

Luckington

- Some Memorial Inscriptions: Luckington, Wiltshire: St. Mary & St. Ethelbert's Churchyard
  www.wishful-thinking.org.uk/Genuki/WIL/Luckington/MIs.html

Lydiard Millicent

- All Saints, Lydiard Millicent, Wiltshire
  www.oodwooc.f9.co.uk/ph__lydmil.htm
  Photographs of inscriptions

Lydiard Tregoze

- St. Mary, Lydiard Tregoze, Wiltshire
  www.oodwooc.f9.co.uk/ph__lt.htm
  Photographs of inscriptions

Lyneham

- St. Michaels & All Angels, Lyneham, Wiltshire
  www.oodwooc.f9.co.uk/ph__lyneham.htm
  Photographs of inscriptions

Malmesbury

- Malmesbury Abbey, Malmesbury, Wiltshire
  www.oodwooc.f9.co.uk/ph__malmesbury.htm
  Photographs of inscriptions

- Some Memorial Inscriptions: Malmesbury, Wiltshire: the Abbey Churchyard and Cemetery
  www.wishful-thinking.org.uk/Genuki/WIL/Malmesbury/MIs.html

Marlborough

- Marlborough, Wiltshire
  www.oodwooc.f9.co.uk/ph__marlborough.htm
  Photographs of inscriptions

Mildenhall

- St. John the Baptist, Mildenhall, Wiltshire
  www.oodwooc.f9.co.uk/ph__mildenhall.htm
  Photographs of inscriptions

Oaksey

- All Saints, Oaksey, Wiltshire
  www.oodwooc.f9.co.uk/ph__oaksey.htm
  Photographs of inscriptions

Odstock

- St. Mary, Odstock, Wiltshire
  www.oodwooc.f9.co.uk/ph__odstock.htm
  Photographs of inscriptions

Ogbourne St. Andrew
- Ogbourne St. Andrew, Wiltshire
  www.oodwooc.f9.co.uk/ph__ogsta.htm
  Photographs of inscriptions

Ogbourne St. George
- Ogbourne St. George, Wiltshire
  www.oodwooc.f9.co.uk/ph__ogstg.htm
  Photographs of inscriptions

Potterne
- St. Mary the Virgin, Potterne, Wiltshire
  www.oodwooc.f9.co.uk/ph__potterne.htm
  Photographs of inscriptions

Poulshot
- St. Peter, Poulshot, Wiltshire
  www.oodwooc.f9.co.uk/ph__poulshot.htm
  Photographs of inscriptions

Preshute
- St. George, Preshute, Wiltshire
  www.oodwooc.f9.co.uk/ph__preshute.htm
  Photographs of inscriptions

Purton
- St. Mary's, Purton, Wiltshire
  www.oodwooc.f9.co.uk/ph__purton.htm
  Photographs of inscriptions

Rockley
- All Saints, Rockley, Wiltshire
  www.oodwooc.f9.co.uk/ph__rockley.htm
  Photographs of inscriptions

Rodbourne
- Holy Rood, Rodbourne, Wiltshire
  www.oodwooc.f9.co.uk/ph__rodbourne.htm
  Photographs of inscriptions

Seagry
- St. Mary the Virgin, Seagry, Wiltshire
  www.oodwooc.f9.co.uk/ph__seagry.htm
  Photographs of inscriptions

Sevenhampton
- St. James, Sevenhampton, Wiltshire
  www.oodwooc.f9.co.uk/ph__sevenh.htm
  Photographs of inscriptions

Sevington
- School at Sevington, Wiltshire
  www.oodwooc.f9.co.uk/ph__sevington.htm
  Photographs of inscriptions

Shaw
- Christ Church, Shaw and Whitley, Wiltshire
  www.oodwooc.f9.co.uk/ph__shaww.htm
  Photographs of inscriptions

Sherston
- Some Memorial Inscriptions: Sherston, Wiltshire: Holy Cross Churchyard
  www.wishful-thinking.org.uk/Genuki/WIL/Sherston/Mls.html

Stanton St. Bernard
- All Saints, Stanton St. Bernard, Wiltshire
  www.oodwooc.f9.co.uk/ph__StantonStB.htm
  Photographs of inscriptions

Stanton St. Quintin
- St. Giles, Stanton St. Quintin, Wiltshire
  www.oodwooc.f9.co.uk/ph__StantonStQ.htm
  Photographs of inscriptions

- Methodist Chapel at Lower Stanton St. Quinton, Wiltshire
  www.oodwooc.f9.co.uk/ph__lowstquin.htm
  Photographs of inscriptions

Stratton St. Margaret
- St Margaret's, Stratton St. Margaret, Wiltshire
  www.oodwooc.f9.co.uk/ph__ssm.htm
  Photographs of inscriptions

Sutton Benger
- All Saints, Sutton Benger, Wiltshire
  www.oodwooc.f9.co.uk/ph__sutbeng.htm
  Photographs of inscriptions

Swindon
- Photographs of Swindon, Wiltshire
  www.oodwooc.f9.co.uk/ph__swindon.htm
  Photographs of inscriptions

Tockenham
- St. Giles, Tockenham, Wiltshire
  www.oodwooc.f9.co.uk/ph__tockenham.htm
  Photographs of inscriptions

Upper Minety
- St. Leonard's, Upper Minety, Wiltshire
  www.oodwooc.f9.co.uk/ph__upminety.htm
  Photographs of inscriptions

Upton Scudamore
- St. Mary's, Upton Scudamore, Wiltshire
  www.oodwooc.f9.co.uk/ph__uptonscud.htm
  Photographs of inscriptions

Wanborough
- St. Andrew, Wanborough, Wiltshire
  www.oodwooc.f9.co.uk/ph__wanborough.htm
  Photographs of inscriptions

West Overton
- St. Michael & All Angels, West Overton, Wiltshire
  www.oodwooc.f9.co.uk/ph__WOverton.htm
  Photographs of inscriptions

Westport
- St. Mary, Westport, Wiltshire
  www.oodwooc.f9.co.uk/ph__westport.htm
  Photographs of inscriptions

Whitley
See Shaw

Winterbourne Bassett
- St. Katharine and St. Peter, Winterbourne Bassett, Wiltshire
  www.oodwooc.f9.co.uk/ph__winterbass.htm
  Photographs of inscriptions

Winterbourne Monkton
- St. Mary Magdalene, Winterbourne Monkton, Wiltshire
  www.oodwooc.f9.co.uk/ph__wintermonk.htm
  Photographs of inscriptions

Wootton Bassett
- St. Bartholomew and All Saints, Wootton Bassett, Wiltshire
  www.oodwooc.f9.co.uk/ph__woottonbassett.htm
  Photographs of inscriptions

Wroughton
- St. John the Baptist and St. Helen, Wroughton, Wiltshire
  www.oodwooc.f9.co.uk/ph__wroughton.htm
  Photographs of inscriptions

Yatton Keynell
- John Aubrey's visit to Yatton Keynell, Wiltshire
  www.oodwooc.f9.co.uk/ph__yatton__aub.htm
  Photographs of inscriptions

Worcestershire

Web Page Collection
- Wishful Thinking's GENUKI: Worcestershire Pages: Memorial Inscription collection
  www.wishful-thinking.org.uk/genuki/WOR/MIs.html

Publications
- B.M.S.G.H. Bookshop: Worcestershire: Parishes, Census Districts, and other places
  www.bmsgh.org/bookshop/worc/wo.a.html
  List of parish registers, monumental inscriptions, *etc.,* published as books and fiche

Brasses
- Monumental Brass Rubbings for England: Worcestershire
  www.ashmol.co.uk/ash/departments/antiquities/brass/
  Click on 'Catalogue' and county. In the Ashmolean Museum, Oxford

- Worcestershire
  www.mbs-brasses.co.uk/Worcestershire.htm
  Bibliography of monumental brasses

Badsey
- Monumental Inscriptions at Badsey St. James
  www.badsey.net/mis/mi__index.htm

Dudley
- St. Thomas, Dudley, Worcs., U.K: Monumental Inscriptions
  uk-transcriptions.accessgenealogy.com/St.Thomas%20MI's.txt

- St. Thomas, Dudley, Worcs., Monumental Inscriptions
  www.platt-grigg.accessgenealogy.com/custom4.html

Eckington
- Some Memorial Inscriptions: Eckington, Worcestershire: Holy Trinity Churchyard
  www.wishful-thinking.org.uk/genuki/WOR/Eckington/MIs.html

Kidderminster
- Kidderminster Cemetery (partial transcription)
  uk-transcriptions.accessgenealogy.com/kidderminster%20Cemetery.htm

Yorkshire

Institutional Collections
- Monumental Inscriptions
  www.doncaster.gov.uk/education/document.asp?WSDOCID=1222
  List of transcriptions held by Doncaster Archives

Indexes
- A Collection of Strays from Many Yorkshire Graveyards and Cemeteries
  www.genuki.org.uk/big/eng/YKS/Misc/MIs/YKS/MelsStraysIndex.html

- The Pontefract & District Family History Society Search Services
  freespace.virgin.net/richard.lockwood/
  Details of parish register and monumental inscription databases *etc.*

Brasses
- Monumental Brass Rubbings for England: Yorkshire
  www.ashmol.co.uk/ash/departments/antiquities/brass/
  Click on 'Catalogue' and county. In the Ashmolean Museum, Oxford

- Yorkshire
  www.mbs-brasses.co.uk/Yorkshire.htm
  Bibliography of monumental brasses

Publications
- Monumental Inscriptions taken from Churches & Churchyards with the Archdeaconry of Doncaster on fiche
  www.doncasterfhs.freeserve.co.uk
  Click on 'Publications' and title

- The City of York and District Family History Society: Society Publications
  www.yorkfamilyhistory.org.uk/books.htm
  Includes monumental inscriptions

Beeston
- Memorials in the Churchyard of St. Mary's Church, Beeston Road, Beeston, Leeds
  freepages.genealogy.rootsweb.com/~framland/beeston/stmb1.htm

Bentley

- Bentley St. Peter's Memorial Inscriptions
  www.doncasterfhs.freeserve.co.uk/members/
  Click on 'Monumental Inscriptions', and go to Bentley. Downloadable file for Doncaster Family History Society members only

Bolsterstone

- Bolsterstone Genealogy Project
  www.bolsterstone.de/Churchyard/MAIN.htm
  Monumental Inscriptions

Bradford

- Bradford Parish Church Graveyard Transcriptions, 2001
  www.genuki.org.uk/big/eng/YKS/bfhs/pcmi.html
  Details of published monumental inscriptions for sale

Bramley

- Memorials in the Churchyard of St. Peter's Church, Hough Lane, Bramley, Leeds
  freepages.genealogy.rootsweb.com/~framland/Bram/stpb1.htm

Campsall

- Campsall Cemetery Monumental Inscriptions
  www.doncasterfhs.freeserve.co.uk/members/
  Click on 'Monumental Inscriptions' and go to Campsall. Downloadable file for Doncaster Family History Society members only

Chapel Allerton

- Some Monumental Inscriptions in Chapel Allerton Cemetery, Leeds
  homepage.ntlworld.com/nev.hurworth/MIsCA.htm

Darton

- Monumental Inscriptions of All Saints Church, Darton
  www.barnsleyfhs.co.uk/dartonintro.htm

Drax

- Drax Saint Peter Churchyard, North Yorkshire, England
  www.interment.net/data/eng/north__yorkshire/drax__stpeter/stpeter.htm

Escrick

- Escrick Saint Helen Churchyard, North Yorkshire, England
  www.interment.net/data/eng/north__yorkshire/escrick__sthelen/sthelen.htm

Farsley

- Farsley: Farsley Baptist MIs Index
  www.genuki.org.uk/big/eng/YKS/Misc/MIs/WRY/FarsleyBaptistMIindex.html

Filey

- Filey Parish: Filey Memorial Plaque Transcriptions
  www.genuki.org.uk/big/eng/YKS/NRY/Filey/MPFileyStOswaldFishermenPlaque.html
  Fishermen's memorial, 1901-48

Guisborough

- Guisbro Saint Nicholas Churchyard, Guisbro, North Yorkshire, England
  www.interment.net/data/eng/north__yorkshire/stnicholas/stnick.htm

Halifax

- Halifax Monumental Inscriptions
  www.genuki.org.uk/big/eng/YKS/Misc/MIs/WRY/HalifaxStPauls.html

- All Souls Church and Cemetery, Halifax
  www.westriding.fsnet.co.uk/allsouls.htm
  Includes some inscriptions

- Friends of Lister Lane Cemetery, Halifax
  www.listerlanecemetery.co.uk/
  Introduction

Hartshead

- Memorial Inscriptions
  freepages.genealogy.rootsweb.com/~hartsheadcumclifton/hartshead/misa.htm
  Continued at **/misb.htm** For Hartshead

- Hartshead Graveyard Map and Survey
  freepages.genealogy.rootsweb.com/~hartsheadcumclifton/hartshead/graveyard__map.htm

High Hoyland
- Memorial Inscriptions of High Hoyland Parish Church in the Diocese of Wakefield
  www.barnsleyfhs.freeserve.co.uk/highhoylandintro.htm

Honley
- Honley Cemetery Burial Book
  website.lineone.net/~gburhouse.book.htm
  Index 1857-1930

- Honley Cemetery, Garden of Rest Memorials
  website.lineone.net/~gburhouse/garden.html

- Honley Monumental Inscriptions
  www.honley.ukf.net/

Horley
- Horley Chapels
  website.lineone.net/~gburhouse/chapels.htm
  Includes inscriptions

Knaresborough
- Knaresborough Cemetery
  gye.future.easyspace.com/KnareCem.htm
  Includes some inscriptions

Lofthouse
- Lofthouse Colliery 1973
  freepages.history.rootsweb.com/~framland/lc.htm
  Memorial to a mining disaster

- Lofthouse Colliery 1973
  gye.future.easyspace.com/cenotaphs/lc.htm

Lythe
- Lythe: Some of the Monumental Inscriptions from the Churchyard (1888)
  www.genuki.org.uk/big/eng/YKS/Misc/Transcriptions/NRY/
                                              Lythe1888MIs.html

Northallerton
- A Study of the Graveyard of Northallerton Upper Cemetery
  www.genuki.org.uk/big/eng/YKS/Misc/NRY/NorthallertonMIsIndex.html

- Northallerton Cemetery
  www.northallertonweb.co.uk/ntoncem/

Ossett
- Memorials in the Burial Ground of the Demolished lst Baptist Church, Baptist Lane, Ossett
  freepages.genealogy.rootsweb.com/~framland/Ossett/obmi1.htm

- Memorials in the Burial Ground of the Demolished Baptist Church, Baptist Lane, Ossett
  freepages.genealogy.rootsweb.com/~framland/Ossett/trans1.htm

Outwood
- Memorials in the Churchyard of St Mary Magdalene Church, Leeds Road, Outwood
  freepages.genealogy.rootsweb.com/~framland/outwood/stmm1.htm

- St. Mary Magdelene Church, Outwood
  freepages.genealogy.rootsweb.com/~framland/CHURCH/smout.htm
  Includes page on 'some memorials in the churchyard'.

Riccall
- Ricall Saint Mary Churchyard, North Yorkshire, England
  www.interment.net/data/eng/north__yorkshire/ricall__stmary/stmary.htm

Ripon
- A Verbatim copy of all the Monuments, Gravestones, and other Sepulchral Memorials in Ripon Cathedral and its burial ground
  www.tic.ch/e-image/andrew/Books/RiponMI/index.html
  Copy of a book originally published 1847

Rosedale
- Rosedale People: an Index
  www.genuki.org.uk/big/eng/YKS/Misc/Transcriptions/NRYRosedale/
                                                      index.html

  Sources indexed include parish registers and monumental inscriptions

- Rosedale Monumental Inscriptions
  www.genuki.org.uk/big/eng/YKS/Misc/MIs/NRY/RosedaleMIs.html

Sandal
- A Couple of Memorials in the Churchyard of St. Helens, Sandal, Wakefield, West Yorkshire
  freepages.genealogy.rootsweb.com/~framland/shs/tr1.htm

Sharrow
- The General Cemetery, Sharrow, Sheffield
  www.shu.ac.uk/web-admin/cemetery/index.html
  Brief introduction

South Milford
- South Milford: South Milford Memorial Inscriptions
  www.genuki.org.uk/big/eng/YKS/Misc/MIs/WRY/
  SouthMilfordGravestones.html

Staincross
- Memorials in the Burial Ground of St. John the Evangelist, Staincross
  freepages.genealogy.rootsweb.com/~framland/stcr/stjsc1.htm

Thornes
- Memorials in St. James Church, Thornes, Wakefield, West Yorkshire, England
  freepages.genealogy.rootsweb.com/~framland/tmi.htm

Tickhill
- Tickhill Monumental Inscriptions
  www.doncasterfhs.freeserve.co.uk/members/
  Click on 'Monumental Inscriptions' and go to Tickhill. Downloadable file for Doncaster Family History Society members only

Wakefield
- Wakefield Council's Cemeteries and Crematoria Pages
  www.wakefield.gov.uk/community/psd/Cems__home.htm
  Brief information on 19 cemeteries

- Churches in the Wakefield Area of West Yorkshire, England
  freepages.genealogy.rootsweb.com/~framland/CHURCH/church.htm
  Many pages, but few inscriptions

- Dedications
  freepages.history.rootsweb.com/~framland/Dedic.htm
  Inscriptions on benches at Thornes Park, Wakefield

Worsbrough
- Index to the Monumental Inscriptions of St. Mary's Church, Worsbrough
  www.barnsleyfhs.co.uk/wmi1.htm
  Continued on 3 further pages

York
- York Cemetery Homepage
  homepages.tesco.net/~hugh.murray/home.htm
  Introduction only

- York Cemetery Trust
  gye.future.easyspace.com/yorkct.htm
  Brief history

Wales

General
- Welsh for Monumental Inscriptions
  www.westwales.co.uk/dfhs/helpdesk.htm
  Brief glossary

Brasses
- Wales
  www.mbs-brasses.co.uk/Wales.htm
  Bibliography of monumental brasses

Anglesey

Brasses
- Monumental Brass Rubbings for Wales, Anglesey
  www.ashmol.co.uk/ash/departments/antiquities/brass/
  Click on 'Catalogue' and county. In the Ashmolean Museum, Oxford

Breconshire

Publications
- Brecknock Monumental Inscriptions
  archives.powys.gov.uk/lsn/20.html
  List

Publications
- Powys F.H.S. Publications
  www.rootsweb.com/~wlspfhs/powyspub.htm
  Includes many monumental inscriptions

Caernarvonshire

Publications
See Cardiganshire

Brasses
- Monumental Brass Rubbings for Wales: Caernarvonshire
  www.ashmol.co.uk/ash/departments/antiquities/brass/
  Click on 'Catalogue' and county. In the Ashmolean Museum, Oxford

Conway
- Memorial Inscriptions from the St. Mary's Parish Church, Conwy, North Wales
  members.tripod.com/~Caryl__Williams/conwy-7.html

Cardiganshire

Web Page Collections
- Cardiganshire, Wales: Burial Grounds
  www.westwales.co.uk/dfhs/burial/cgninter.htm
  List, with some indexes to monumental inscriptions, separately listed below

- Dyfed Family History Society: Burial Grounds
  www.dyfedfhs.org.uk/copi.htm
  Collection of monumental inscription indexes, separately listed below

Publications
- Indexes and Transcripts for Sale on Fiche: Monumental Inscriptions
  www.Dyfedfhs.org/forsale3.htm
  From Dyfed Family History Society; for Cardiganshire, Carmarthenshire and Pembrokeshire

Brongwyn
- Non-conformist Records: Trewen, Cwm-coy, Brongwyn, CGN
  www.dyfedfhs.org.uk/copi
  Click on name

Cellan
- Non-conformist records: Caeronnen, Cellan, CGN
  www.dyfedfhs.org.uk/copi
  Click on name. Index to monumental inscriptions published by Dyfed Family History Society

- Non-conformist records: Capel Erw, Cellan, CGN
  www.dyfedfhs.org.uk/copi
  Click on name. Index to monumental inscriptions published by Dyfed Family History Society

Llanarth
- Non-conformist records: Pen-Cae, Llanarth, CGN
  www.dyfedfhs.org.uk/copi
  Click on name. Index to monumental inscriptions published by Dyfed Family History Society

- MI Burial Index: St David's, Llanarth, CGN
  www.dyfedfhs.org.uk/copi
  Click on name. Index to monumental inscriptions published by Dyfed Family History Society

Llanddeinol
- M.I. Burial Index: Llanddeinol Parish Church, CGN
  www.dyfedfhs.org.uk/copi
  Click on name. Index to monumental inscriptions published by Dyfed Family History Society

Llandysiliogogo
- Non-conformist records: Neuadd Calvinist, Llandysiliogogo, CGN
  www.dyfedfhs.org.uk/copi
  Click on name. Index to monumental inscriptions published by Dyfed Family History Society

Llandysul
- Llandysul Churchyard Cemetery, Dyfed County, Wales
  interment.net/data/wales/dyfed/llandysul/llandysul.htm

Llanbadarn Faws
- Llanbadarn Fawr Memorial Records
  freepages.genealogy.rootsweb.com/~ceredigwynd/
  llanbf-memorial-list.html

Llangynfelyn
- Memorials in the Cemeteries
  www.llangynfelyn.dabsol.co.uk/dogfennau/mynwentydd__mynegiad.html
  At Llangynfelyn

Llanina
- M.I. Burial Index: Llanina Parish Church, CGN
  www.dyfedfhs.org.uk
  Click on name. Index to monumental inscriptions published by Dyfed Family History Society

- Non-conformist records: Wern, Llanina, CGN
  www.dyfedfhs.org.uk
  Click on name. Index to monumental inscriptions published by Dyfed Family History Society

Llechryd

- M.I. Burial Index: Llechryd Parish Church, CGN
  www.dyfedfhs.org.uk/copi
  Click on name. Index to monumental inscriptions published by Dyfed Family History Society

Mwnt

- M.I. Burial Index: Mwnt Parish Church, CGN
  www.dyfedfhs.org.uk/copi
  Click on name. Index to monumental inscriptions published by Dyfed Family History Society

Tremain

- M.I. Burial Index: Tremain Parish Church, CGN
  www.dyfedfhs.org.uk/copi
  Click on name. Index to monumental inscriptions published by Dyfed Family History Society

Carmarthenshire

Web Page Collections

- Carmarthenshire, Wales: Burial Grounds
  www.westwales.co.uk/dfhs/burial.cmninter.htm
  List, with some indexes to monumental inscriptions, separately listed below

Llandyfeisant

- Monumental Inscriptions Index: Llandyfeisant Parish Church, CMN
  www.westwales.co.uk/dfhs/burial/cmnildft.htm
  Index to monumental inscriptions published by Dyfed Family History Society

Llanycrwys

- Monumental Inscriptions Index: Llanycrwys Parish Church, CMN
  www.westwales.co.uk/dfhs/burial/cmnilyws.htm
  Index to monumental inscriptions published by Dyfed Family History Society

Llansawel

- Monumental Inscriptions Index: Llansawel Parish Church, CMN
  www.westwales.co.uk/dfhs/burial/cmnilswl.htm
  Index to monumental inscriptions published by Dyfed Family History Society

Flint and Denbighshire

Brasses
- Monumental Brass Rubbings for Wales, Denbighshire
  www.ashmol.co.uk/ash/departments/antiquities/brass/
  Click on 'Catalogue' and county. In the Ashmolean Museum, Oxford

Publications
- Miscellaneous Publications by Clwyd F.H.S.
  www.clwydfhs.org.uk/misc__pubs.html
  Includes monumental inscriptions from Flintshire and Denbighshire

Glamorganshire

Institutional Collections
- Monumental Inscriptions at Cardiff Central Library
  home.clara.net/tirbach/HelpPageCardiffDirs.html#MONUMENTAL

Indexes
- Cemetery Surname Indexes, Glamorgan, Wales
  freespace.virgin.net/freebies/glammi.htm
  List of surnames found on fiche transcriptions of monumental
  inscriptions for six churches and chapels in Merthyr, Rhondda, Crug
  Olas, Oystermouth, Swansea, and Church Village

Web Page Collections
- Nicholas History, Wales
  homepage.ntlworld.com/stephen.nicholas
  Collection of monumental inscription web pages for Glamorganshire,
  individually listed below

Brasses
- Monumental Brass Rubbings for Wales: Glamorgan
  www.ashmol.co.uk/ash/departments/antiquities/brass/
  Click on 'Catalogue' and county. In the Ashmolean Museum, Oxford

Publications
- Glamorgan Family History Society Booklet Publications: Monumental
  Inscriptions
  www.rootsweb.com/~wlsglfhs/books2.htm

- Glamorgan Family History Society Microfiche Publications
  www.rootsweb.com/~wlsglfhs/fiche2.htm
  Includes monumental inscriptions

Bettws
- Sardis Baptist Chapel, Bettws, Nr. Bridgend, Glamorgan, Wales, United
  Kingdom
  www.oldroots.co.uk/inscriptions
  Click on 'Glamorgan and Bettws'

Caerphilly
- Groeswen (Monumental Inscriptions)
  homepage.ntlworld.com/stephen.nicholas/
  Click on title. At Caerphilly

- Tonyfelin-Caerphilly Monumental Inscriptions
  homepage.ntlworld.com/stephen.nicholas/PAGE14.HTML

- Monumental Inscriptions, Watford Ind. Chapel, Caerphilly
  homepages.ntlworld.com/stephen.nicholas/
  Click on title

Cardiff
- Cardiff Records, volume III, chapter XI: Ecclesiastical Memorial
  Inscriptions
  www.btinternet.com/~pat.sewell/cr/cr-memorial-inscriptions.html

- Monumental Inscriptions, St. John Baptist, Cardiff
  homepage.ntlworld.com/stephen.nicholas/
  Click on title

Cowbridge
- Memorials at Holy Cross Churchyard, Cowbridge, Glamorgan
  www.genuki.org.uk/big/wal/GLA/Cowbridge/Cowbridge.Chyard.MI.html

- Memorials at Cowbridge Cemetery, Glamorgan
  www.genuki.org.uk/big/wal/GLA/Cowbridge/Cowbridge.MI.html

Eglwysilan
- St. Ilan, Eglwysilan (Monumental Inscriptions)
  homepage.ntlworld.com/stephen.nicholas/
  Click on title

Llanbleddian
- Memorials at St. John the Baptist Churchyard, Llanbleddian
  www.genuki.org.uk/big/wal/GLA/Llanbleddian/Llanbleddian.MI.html

Llanfrynach
- Memorials at Llanfrynach Churchyard, Glamorgan
  www.genuki.org.uk/big/wal/GLA/Penllyn/Llanfrynach/MI.html

Llanharan
- Llanharan Cemetery, Glamorgan, Wales, United Kingdom
  www.oldroots.co.uk/inscriptions/
  Click on 'Glamorgan' and 'Llanharan'

Llanishen
- Monumental Inscriptions, St. Isan, Llanishen
  homepage.ntlworld.com/steve.nick/Page5.html

- Monumental Inscriptions: St. Isan, Llanishen
  homepage.ntlworld.com/steve.nick/Page6.html

Llantwit Juxta Neath
- Parish of Llantwit Juxta Neath: Church of St. Illtyd
  homepage.ntlworld.com/g.brian.wagstaffe/textfile.htm
  List of graves

St. Brides super Ely
- St. Brides-super-Ely, Vale of Glamorgan, Wales: The Parish Cemetery
  www.tnhillbillie.net/wales/stbrides/english/cemetery/index.html
  Includes list of surnames from inscriptions

St. Mary Church
- Memorials at St. Mary Church
  www.genuki.org.uk/big/wal/GLA/StMaryChurch/MI.html

Taffs Well
- Taff's Well Cemetery, Glamorgan, Wales, United Kingdom
  www.oldroots.co.uk/inscriptions/
  Click on 'Glamorgan' and 'Taffs Well'

Trealaw
- Trealaw Cemetery Index
  www.trealawcemetery.co.uk
  Click on 'Glamorgan' and 'Trealaw'

Whitchurch
- Monumental Inscriptions: St. Mary (Old Burial Ground) Whitchurch
  homepage.ntlworld.com/steve/nick/Page4.html

Ystradowen
- Memorials at Ystradowen Churchyard, Glamorgan
  www.genuki.org.uk/big/wal/GLA/Ystradowen/Ystradowen.MI.html

Ystradyfodwg
- Penrhys Cemetery Index
  www.jones5512.freeserve.co.uk/penrhys.htm
  In Ystradyfodwg parish, Glamorganshire

- Neba Chapel, Ystrad
  www.jones5512.freeserve.co.uk/Nebo%20Chapel/nebo%20front.htm
  Burials transferred to Penrhys Cemetery

Merionethshire

No Web pages identified

Monmouthshire

Institutional Collections
- List of Monmouthshire Monumental Inscriptions
  www.genuki.org.uk/big/wal/MON/MI__List.html
  Held by the Society of Genealogists

Web Collections
- Wishful Thinking's GENUKI: Monmouthshire Page: Memorial
  Inscription Collection
  www.wishful-thinking.org.uk/genuki/MON/Mls.html
  Particular pages listed individually below

Brasses
- Monumental Brass Rubbings for Wales: Monmouthshire
  www.ashmol.co.uk/ash/departments/antiquities/brass/
  Click on 'Catalogue' and county. In the Ashmolean Museum, Oxford

Publications
- Monumental Inscriptions: list of Fiche
  www.rootsweb.com/~wlsgfhs/Sales/MlsAlpha.htm
  Available from Gwent Family History Society

Caldicot
- Some Memorial Inscriptions: Caldicot, Monmouthshire: St. Mary's
  Churchyard
  www.wishful-thinking.org.uk/Genuki/MON/Caldicot/Mls.html

Llandenny
- Some Memorial Inscriptions: Llandenny, Monmouthshire: St. John the
  Apostle's Churchyard
  www.wishful-thinking.org.uk/Genuki/MON/Llandenny/Mls.html

Llangattock Vibon Avel
- Some Memorial Inscriptions: Llangattock-Vibon-Avel, Monmouthshire:
  St. Cadoc's Churchyard
  www.wishful-thinking.org.uk/Genuki/MON/LlangattockVibonAvel/Mls.html

Llanhilleth
- Survey of Graveyard Inscriptions at St. Illtyd: Old Church, Llanhilleth,
  near Abertillery, Gwent, South Wales
  www.illtyd.freeserve.co.uk/friends/graves4.html

Mitchel Troy
- Some Memorial Inscriptions: Mitchel Troy Monmouthshire: St. Michael's
  Churchyard
  www.wishful-thinking.org.uk/Genuki/MON/MitchelTroy/Mls.html

Montgomeryshire

Institutional Collections
- Montgomeryshire Monumental Inscriptions
  archives.powys.gov.uk/lsn/21.html
  List

Pembrokeshire

Web Page Collections
- Pembrokeshire, Wales, Burial Grounds
  www.westwales.co.uk/dfhs/burial/peminter.htm
  List, with one index to monumental inscriptions, separately listed below
  (more will no doubt follow)

Brasses
- Monumental Brass Rubbings for Wales: Pembrokeshire
  www.ashmol.co.uk/ash/departments/antiquities/brass/
  Click on 'Catalogue' and county. In the Ashmolean Museum, Oxford

Camrose
- Monumental Inscriptions at Camrose
  www.rootsweb.com/~wlscfhs/camrosemis.pdf

Haverfordwest
- Some Memorial Inscriptions: Haverfordwest, Pembrokeshire: City Road
  Cemetery
  www.wishful-thinking.org.uk/genuki/PEM/Haverfordwest/MIs.html

Meline
- Monumental Inscriptions Index: Meline Parish Church, Pembrokeshire
  www.westwales.co.uk/dfhs/burial/pemimeli.htm

Rudbaxton
- Monumental Inscriptions at Rudbaxton
  www.rootsweb.com/~wlscfhs/rudbaxmis.pdf

Radnorshire

Institutional Collections
- Radnorshire Monumental Inscriptions
  archives.powys.gov.uk/lsn/22.html
  List